Carnegie Learning Geometry

Student Assignments

D1279456

Carnegie Learning

Carnegie Learning >

437 Grant St., Suite 918
Pittsburgh, PA 15219
Phone 412.690.2442
Customer Service Phone 877.401.2527
Fax 412.690.2444

www.carnegielearning.com

Acknowledgments

We would like to thank those listed here who helped prepare the *Carnegie Learning Math Series*.

Carnegie Learning Authoring Team
- Sandy Bartle, Senior Academic Officer
- David Dengler, Sr. Director, Curriculum Development
- Joshua Fisher, Math Editor
- John Fitsioris, Curriculum Developer
- Beth Karambelkar, Curriculum Developer
- David "Augie" Rivera, Math Editor
- Lezlee Ross, Curriculum Developer

Contributing Authors
- Jaclyn Snyder
- Dr. Mary Lou Metz

Vendors
- Cenveo® Publisher Services
- Mathematical Expressions
- Bookmasters, Inc.
- Hess Print Solutions
- Bradford & Bigelow
- Mind Over Media
- Lapiz
- eInstruction

Special Thanks
- Carnegie Learning Managers of School Partnership for content and design review.
- CL Software Development Team for research and content review.
- William S. Hadley for his mentoring leadership and pedagogical pioneering in mathematics education.
- Amy Jones Lewis for content review.

ISBN: 978-1-60972-218-0
Student Assignments, Geometry

Printed in the United States of America
2-07/2013 B&B

Name _____ Date _____

Let's Get This Started!
Points, Lines, Planes, Rays, and Line Segments

1. Identify each of the following in the figure shown.

   a. Name all points.

   b. Name all lines.

   c. Name all planes.

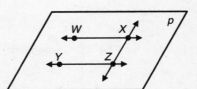

2. Identify each of the following in the figure shown.

   a. Name all collinear points.

   b. Name all coplanar lines.

   c. Name all skew lines.

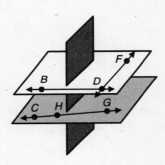

3. Identify each of the following in the figure shown.

   a. Name all rays and identify each endpoint.

   b. Name all line segments and identify the endpoints.

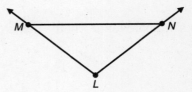

4. Explain the differences among sketching a geometric figure, drawing a geometric figure, and constructing a geometric figure.

5. Sketch two planes whose intersection is a line.

6. Sketch three planes whose intersection is a point.

7. Draw and label three collinear points *X*, *Y*, and *Z* such that point *Y* is between points *X* and *Z* and the distance between points *X* and *Y* is one half the distance between points *Y* and *Z*.

8. Use a symbol to represent the name of each geometric figure.

    a.

    b.

    c.

Name _____ Date _____

Let's Move!
Translating and Constructing Line Segments

Use the map of Smalltown to answer each question. One mile is equal to 6 units on the map.

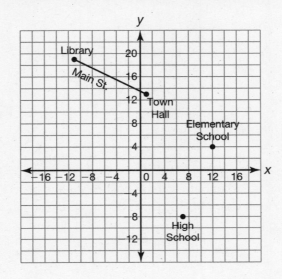

1. After school today, Mica must walk from the high school to the elementary school to pick up his younger brother.

   a. Determine the distance between the high school and the elementary school.

   b. How many miles must Mica walk to pick up his younger brother?

2. The coordinates for the points that mark the locations of the grocery store and the post office can be determined by translating Main Street vertically 15 units down. The grocery store is located directly south of the town hall.

   a. What are the coordinates of the points that mark the location of the grocery store and the post office? Explain how you determined your answers. Then, plot the points on the coordinate plane.

   b. What must be true about the road between the post office and grocery store and Main Street? Explain how you determined your answer. Then, use mathematics to verify your answer.

3. The town would like to construct a park that is one mile from the town hall. Use your compass to show all possible locations for the new park. Explain how you determined your answer.

Name _____ Date _____

Treasure Hunt
Midpoints and Bisectors

The grid shows the locations of a sandbox and a fountain in a park. Each grid square represents a square that is one meter long and one meter wide.

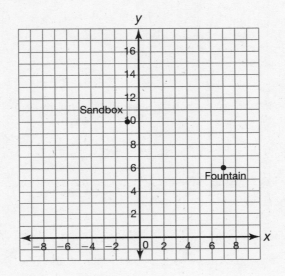

1. Calculate the distance between the sandbox and the fountain.

2. You decide to meet your friend halfway between the fountain and sandbox.

   a. Calculate the midpoint of the line segment that passes through the point representing the sandbox and the point representing the fountain. Then, plot the point.

   b. Verify your calculations in part (a) by constructing the midpoint of the line connecting the sandbox and the fountain.

3. The swings are located at $(-4, 7)$, which is halfway between the sandbox and the slide.

   a. Plot and label the point representing the swings.

   b. Calculate the location of the slide. Show your work. Then, plot and label the point representing the slide.

   c. Verify your calculations in part (b) by constructing the midpoint of the line connecting the sandbox and the slide.

Name _____ Date _____

It's All About Angles
Translating and Constructing Angles and Angle Bisectors

1. Point *K* in ∠*JKL* has been translated to Quadrant III to create image *K'*. Describe and perform the translation(s) needed to translate ∠*JKL* to Quadrant III.

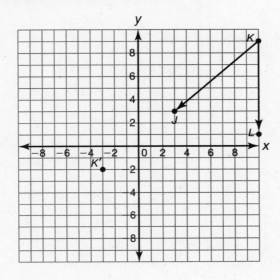

   a. Describe how you can translate the angle to Quadrant III.

   b. Determine what the coordinates will be for points *J'*, *K'*, and *L'* before translating the angle. Explain how you determined your answers.

   c. Verify your answers to part (b) by translating ∠*JKL* to Quadrant III.

2. Perform the construction(s) needed to duplicate ∠*JKL* to create ∠*J'K'L'*.

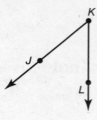

K'
•

    a. Describe how to duplicate ∠*JKL*.

    b. Duplicate ∠*JKL* using construction.

Name _____ Date _____

3. Analyze ∠X.

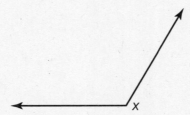

    a. Explain how to construct an angle that is one-fourth the measure of ∠X using only your compass and straightedge.

    b. Construct an angle that is one-fourth the measure of ∠X. Label the angle as ∠WXY.

Name _____ Date _____

Did You Find a Parking Space?
Parallel and Perpendicular Lines on the Coordinate Plane

Christopher is a developer and plans to build a new community development. Use the grid to help
Christopher create a map for his development. Each gridline represents one block.

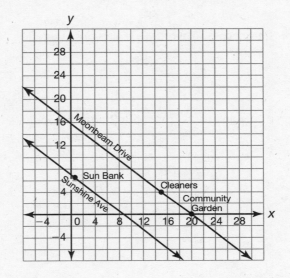

1. Currently there are two main roads that pass through the development and are parallel to each other:
   Sunshine Avenue and Moonbeam Drive.

   a. Calculate the slope of Moonbeam Drive. Show your work.

   b. Determine the slope of Sunshine Avenue. Explain your reasoning.

2. Christopher wants to build a road named, Stargazer Boulevard that will be parallel to Moonbeam Drive. On this road, he will build a new diner located 7 blocks north of the Community Garden.

    a. Identify the coordinates of the new diner and plot the diner on the grid. Explain how you determined the coordinates of the new diner.

    b. Determine the slope of Stargazer Boulevard. Explain your reasoning.

    c. Determine the equation of the line that represents Stargazer Boulevard.

    d. Draw and label Stargazer Boulevard on the grid.

3. Christopher wants to build a road named Rocket Drive that connects Sun Bank to Moonbeam Drive. He wants this road to be as short as possible.

    a. Write an equation for the line representing Rocket Drive. Show your work. Then draw and label Rocket Drive on the grid.

Name _____ Date _____

b. What is the equation of the line representing Moonbeam Drive?
Explain how you determined your answer.

c. Calculate the point of intersection of Rocket Drive and Moonbeam Drive. Show your work.

d. What is the distance from Sun Bank to Moonbeam Drive? Show your work.

Name _____ Date _____

Making Copies—Just as Perfect as the Original!
Constructing Perpendicular Lines, Parallel Lines, and Polygons

1. Construct rectangle *ABCD* so that it is not a square using the given side lengths.

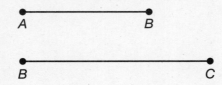

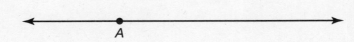

a. Explain how you know that $\overleftrightarrow{AD}$ and $\overleftrightarrow{BC}$ are parallel.

2. Consider line *JK* and point *M*.

a. Write a paragraph to explain how you can construct parallelogram *JKLM* using the given point and line so that the parallelogram is *not* a rectangle.

b. Construct the parallelogram.

Name _____ Date _____

3. The perimeter of an isosceles triangle is shown.

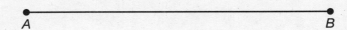

A   B

a. Write a paragraph to explain how you will construct this triangle.

b. Construct the isosceles triangle.

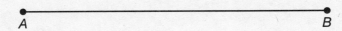

A   B

c. Can you construct more than one isosceles triangle using the given perimeter? Explain your reasoning.

1

Name _____ Date _____

What's the Point?
Points of Concurrency

Use a compass and straightedge to perform each construction.

1. Construct the incenter of △DEF.

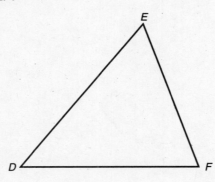

2. Construct the circumcenter of △ABC.

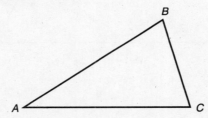

3. Construct the circumcenter of △DEF.

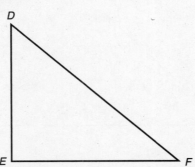

4. Construct the circumcenter of △GHI.

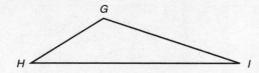

5. Construct the centroid of △ABC.

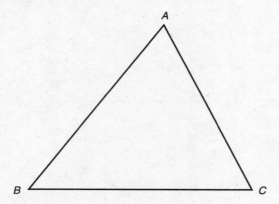

6. Construct the orthocenter of △JKL.

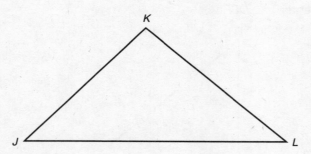

Name _____ Date _____

7. Write the term that best completes each statement.

  a. The incenter of a triangle is the point of concurrency of the _____ of a triangle.

  b. The circumcenter of a triangle is the point of concurrency of the _____ of a triangle.

  c. The centroid of a triangle is the point of concurrency of the _____ of a triangle.

  d. The orthocenter of a triangle is the point of concurrency of the _____ of a triangle.

8. Triangle *FGH* has vertices *F*(−4, 2), *G*(4, 2), and *H*(4, −2).

   a. Use algebra to locate the centroid of △*FGH*.

Name _____ Date _____

b. Use algebra to locate the circumcenter of △*FGH*.

Name _____ Date _____

A Little Dash of Logic
Foundations for Proof

1. Joseph reads a journal article that states that yogurt with live cultures greatly helps digestion and prevents problems associated with lactose intolerance. He notices that his mother has problems with digestion and is lactose intolerant. He suggests that she try eating yogurt because he thinks it may help her feel better.

   a. What is the specific information in this situation?

   b. What is the general information in this situation?

   c. What is the conclusion in this situation?

   d. Did Joseph use inductive reasoning or deductive reasoning to make his conclusion? Explain your reasoning.

   e. Is Joseph's conclusion correct? Explain your reasoning.

2. Chaun is looking through records at a record store with her friend Ronaldo. She comes across a record she has not heard by a band she enjoys. Ronaldo knows that Chaun has five records at home by this band and that she likes all of them. He concludes that she will probably like any record made by this band. He tells Chaun so. She buys the record, saying to herself, "I will probably like this record, because I like records made by this band."

a. What conclusion did Ronaldo make? Why?

b. What type of reasoning did Ronaldo use? Explain your reasoning.

c. What conclusion did Chaun make? Why?

d. What type of reasoning did Chaun use? Explain your reasoning.

e. Is Ronaldo's conclusion definitely true? Is Chaun's conclusion definitely true? Explain your reasoning.

Name _____ Date _____

3. Use the following statement to answer each question.

The sum of the measures of angle *A* and angle *B* is 90 degrees. Therefore, the angles are complementary.

a. Write the conditional statement in propositional form.

b. Identify the hypothesis and the conclusion of the conditional statement.

c. If the hypothesis and conclusion of the conditional statement are both false, what does this mean in terms of the conditional statement?

d. What is the truth value of the conditional statement if the hypothesis and conclusion are both false?

4. Sketch a figure to illustrate the given conditional statement. Then rewrite the conditional statement by separating the hypothesis and conclusion into "Given" information and "Prove" information.

If $\angle AXB$ is a right angle and $\overrightarrow{XY}$ bisects $\angle AXB$, then $m\angle AXY = 45°$ and $m\angle BXY = 45°$.

Given:

Prove:

Name _____ Date _____

And Now From a New Angle
Special Angles and Postulates

1. Use a protractor to draw a pair of supplementary angles that do not share a common side. Label each angle with its measure.

2. Use a protractor to draw a pair of complementary angles that share a common side. Label each angle with its measure.

3. Suppose that $m\angle A = 66°$, $\angle B$ is complementary to $\angle A$, and $\angle C$ is supplementary to $\angle B$. What are the measures of angles B and C?

4. The variables *x* and *y* in the figure represent the measures of angles. Solve for *x* and *y*.

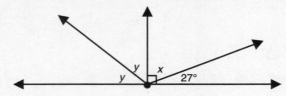

5. The variables *a* and *b* in the figure represent the measures of angles. Solve for *a* and *b*.

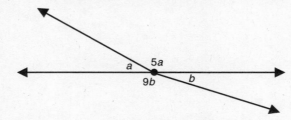

6. Name all pairs of adjacent angles in the figure.

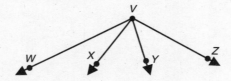

7. What is the difference between two supplementary angles and two angles that form a linear pair?

Name _____ Date _____

8. Identify each of the following in the figure.

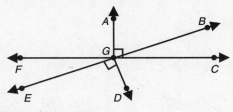

a. Name two pairs of complementary angles.

b. Name six pairs of supplementary angles.

c. Name four pairs of angles that form linear pairs.

d. Name two pairs of vertical angles.

2

9. Sketch and label a figure to illustrate the Linear Pair Postulate. Then use the Linear Pair Postulate to write a symbolic statement about the figure.

10. Use the Segment Addition Postulate to write four different statements about the figure shown.

11. Name the postulate that tells you that $m\angle FGH + m\angle HGJ = m\angle FGJ$ in the figure shown.

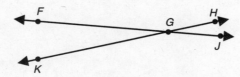

Name _____ Date _____

Forms of Proof
Paragraph Proof, Two-Column Proof, Construction Proof, and Flow Chart Proof

2

1. Identify the property that justifies each statement.

   a. If $\overline{AB} \cong \overline{PR}$ and $\overline{PR} \cong \overline{ST}$, then $\overline{AB} \cong \overline{ST}$.

   b. If $JK = 6$ centimeters and $CD = 6$ centimeters, then $JK = CD$.

   c. Angle ABC is congruent to angle ABC.

   d. If $m\angle 3 = m\angle 1$, then $m\angle 3 + m\angle 2 = m\angle 1 + m\angle 2$.

2. Enter the reasons to complete the two-column proof below.

Given: $\angle 1 \cong \angle 4$
Prove: $\angle 2 \cong \angle 3$

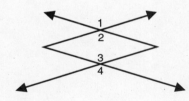

Statements	Reasons
1. $\angle 1 \cong \angle 4$	**1.**
2. $\angle 4 \cong \angle 3$	**2.**
3. $\angle 1 \cong \angle 2$	**3.**
4. $\angle 1 \cong \angle 3$	**4.**
5. $\angle 2 \cong \angle 3$	**5.**

© Carnegie Learning

3. The boxes below show the parts of a flow chart proof. Rearrange the boxes and draw arrows to connect the boxes in a logical sequence to prove the statement.

Given: $FG = JK$

Given: $GH = HJ$

Prove: $FH = HK$

F ●————————————— ● G ● H ● J —————— ● K

$FG + GH = GH + JK$ Addition Property of Equality	$FH = HK$ Substitution	$FG = JK$ Given
$GH = HJ$ Given	$HJ + JK = HK$ Segment Addition Postulate	$GH = GH$ Identity Property
$FG + GH = HJ + JK$ Substitution	$FG + GH = FH$ Segment Addition Postulate	

Name _____ Date _____

4. Write a paragraph proof to prove the statement.

   Given: $m\angle QRS = 90°$

   Given: $\angle RTS \cong \angle QRT$

   Prove: $\angle RTS$ and $\angle TRS$ are complementary.

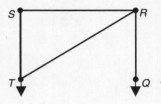

5. Use a construction to prove the statement.

   Given: Line ST is a perpendicular bisector of $\overline{XZ}$.

   Given: $XV = WZ$

   Prove: $VY = YW$

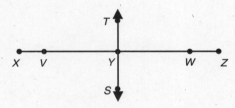

6. In the figure, $\angle GXF \cong \angle CXD$.

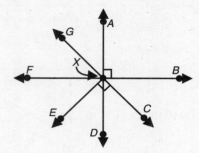

a. What theorem tells you that $\angle AXG \cong \angle CXD$?

b. What theorem tells you that $\angle EXF \cong \angle EXD$?

c. What theorem tells you that $\angle GXD \cong \angle CXF$?

Name _____ Date _____

What's Your Proof?
Angle Postulates and Theorems

1. Use the given information to determine the measures of each of the numbered angles.

   a. $p \parallel q$ and $m\angle 1 = 54°$

   b. $s \parallel t$ and $m\angle 1 = 137°$

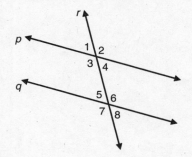
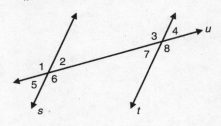

2. Write an expression for the measure of each numbered angle in the figure.

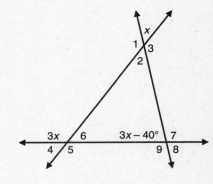

3. Solve for *x* in each figure.

a.

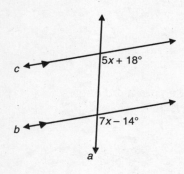

b.

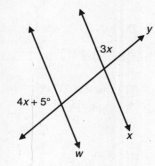

4. Suppose that two parallel lines are intersected by a transversal and all corresponding angles are supplementary. How is this possible? Sketch and label a figure to support your answer.

Name _____ Date _____

5. Determine the relationship between the indicated angles and write a postulate or theorem that justifies your answer.

a. Angles 2 and 8

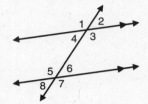

b. Angles 6 and 7

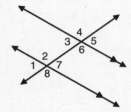

c. Angles 1 and 4

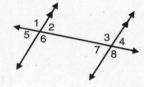

d. Angles 4 and 5

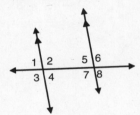

6. What postulate or theorem tells you that $x + y = 180°$ in the figure shown?

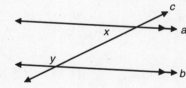

7. The following boxes show the parts of a flow chart proof of the Same-Side Interior Angle Theorem. Rearrange the boxes and draw arrows to connect the boxes in a logical sequence to prove the Same-Side Interior Angle Theorem.

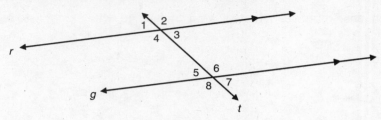

Angles 1 and 4 are a linear pair.
Linear Pair Postulate

$m\angle 1 = m\angle 5$
Definition of congruent angles

$r \parallel g$
Given

$\angle 5$ and $\angle 4$ are supplementary
Definition of supplementary angles

$m\angle 5 + m\angle 4 = 180°$
Substitution

$m\angle 1 + m\angle 4 = 180°$
Definition of linear pair

$\angle 1 \cong \angle 5$
Corresponding Angles Postulate

Name _____ Date _____

8. Use the figure to determine the measure of each indicated angle.

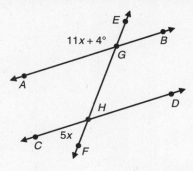

   a. m∠EGA   **b.** m∠CHF

   c. m∠FHD   **d.** m∠EGB

9. Suppose that two parallel lines are intersected by a transversal and all same side interior angles are congruent. How is this possible? Sketch and label a figure to support your answer.

Name _____ Date _____

A Reversed Condition
Parallel Line Converse Theorems

1. Use the figure to write the postulate or theorem that justifies each statement.

    a. $m\angle 1 = m\angle 8$, so $a \parallel b$

    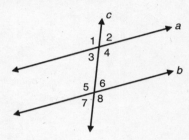

    b. $m\angle 4 + m\angle 6 = 180°$, so $a \parallel b$

    c. $a \parallel b$, so $m\angle 3 = m\angle 7$

    d. $m\angle 2 + m\angle 8 = 180°$, so $a \parallel b$

    e. $m\angle 4 = m\angle 5$, so $a \parallel b$

    f. $a \parallel b$, so $m\angle 3 + m\angle 5 = 180°$

2. Use the given information to determine the pair of lines that are parallel. Write the postulate or theorem that justifies your answer.

    a. $m\angle 4 = m\angle 5$

    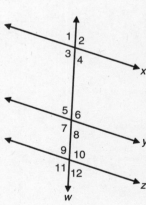

    b. $m\angle 2 + m\angle 12 = 180°$

    c. $m\angle 7 = m\angle 11$

    d. $m\angle 8 + m\angle 10 = 180°$

    e. $m\angle 1 + m\angle 7 = 180°$

    f. $m\angle 2 = m\angle 11$

3. Given triangle *ABC* as shown, prove that segment *AB* is parallel to segment *DE*.

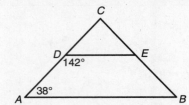

Name _____ Date _____

4. In the figure, $m\angle 1 = (7x - 12)°$, $m\angle 3 = (6x + 4)°$, and $m\angle 8 = (5x)°$. Show that line p is parallel to line q. Explain your reasoning.

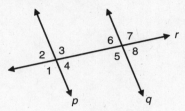

Name _____ Date _____

Transforming to a New Level!
Using Transformations to Determine Area

1. Franco translates rectangle *JKLM* so that it has one vertex on the origin. The result is rectangle *J'K'L'M'*. He claims that he doesn't have to use the Distance Formula to help him calculate the perimeter and the area of this translated rectangle.

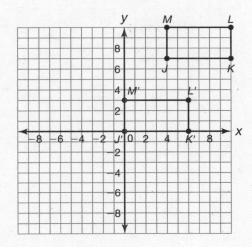

a. Is Franco correct? Why or why not?

b. Maeko claims that you don't have to use the Distance Formula *or* translate the rectangle in order to calculate the perimeter and the area of the original rectangle. Is she correct? Why or why not?

c. Give an example of a case in which translating a rectangle would be extremely helpful in simplifying the calculations for determining the perimeter and area of the rectangle.

2. Olivia translates rectangle *WXYZ* vertically up 1 unit and horizontally to the right 4 units to produce the image *W'X'Y'Z'*. Thom translates the rectangle vertically up 6 units and horizontally to the right 5 units to produce the image *W"X"Y"Z"*.

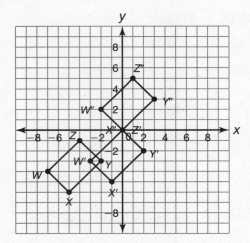

a. Would you prefer to use Olivia's translation or Thom's translation to determine the perimeter and the area of the rectangle? Explain your reasoning.

b. Calculate the perimeter and the area of the rectangle. Show your work.

Name _____ Date _____

Looking at Something Familiar in a New Way
Area and Perimeter of Triangles on the Coordinate Plane

1. Cisco claims that $\overline{GH}$ is the height of triangle *EFG*, and Beth claims that $\overline{GJ}$ is the height of triangle *EFG*.

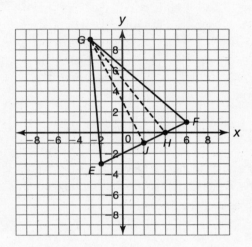

a. Who is correct? Support your answer with mathematics.

   b. Calculate the area of triangle *EFG*. Show your work.

2. A few years ago, Leon planted a small triangular garden in his backyard. Recently, he has been thinking that the garden is too small. Now, he wants to double the area of the garden. His original garden is shown on the coordinate plane. Each unit represents one square foot.

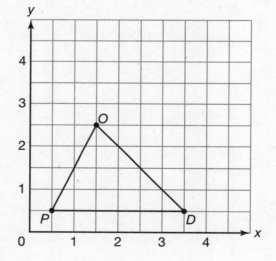

Name _____ Date _____

    a. Describe two ways Leon could double the area of his garden.

    b. Because of the location of Leon's neighbors, he cannot extend the garden any farther horizontally. Use this information to manipulate the pre-image *POD* representing Leon's garden to double the area. Label the image as *PO'D*.

    c. Determine the area of the original garden and the new garden to verify that the area has doubled.

Name _____ Date _____

Grasshoppers Everywhere!
Area and Perimeter of Parallelograms on the Coordinate Plane

1. Joel knows that the formulas to determine the areas of rectangles and non-rectangular parallelograms are the same. He multiplies the lengths of $\overline{WX}$ and $\overline{WZ}$ to determine the area of parallelogram *WXYZ*.

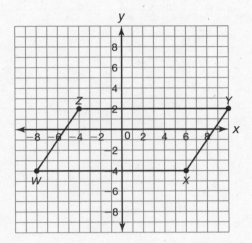

    a. Has Joel correctly determined the area of the parallelogram? Explain your reasoning.

    b. Calculate the area of parallelogram *WXYZ*. Show your work.

2. Parallelograms *JKLM* and *JKPR* are given. Without calculating the areas, determine whether or not the area of parallelogram *JKPR* is twice that of the area of parallelogram *JKLM*. Explain how you determined your answer.

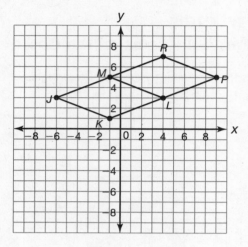

Name _____ Date _____

Leavin' on a Jet Plane
Area and Perimeter of Trapezoids on the Coordinate Plane

1. Trapezoid *QRST* is given.

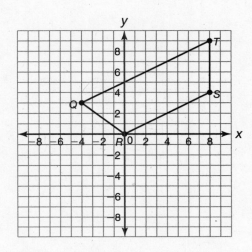

a. Determine the perimeter of trapezoid *QRST*. Show your work. Round your answer to the nearest hundredth.

b. Determine the area of trapezoid *QRST*. Show your work and explain how you determined your answer.

Name _____ Date _____

Composite Figures on the Coordinate Plane
Area and Perimeter of Composite Figures on the Coordinate Plane

1. Composite figure *ABCDEFG* is given.

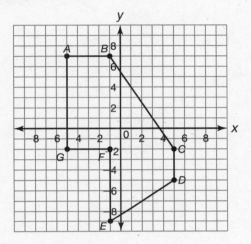

a. Determine the perimeter of figure *ABCDEFG*.

b. Determine the area of figure *ABCDEFG*.

Name _____ Date _____

Whirlygigs for Sale!
Rotating Two-Dimensional Figures through Space

The ChocoWorld Candy Company is going to enter a candy competition in which they will make a structure entirely out of chocolate. They are going to build a fairytale castle using several different molds, and they need to make the molds using a drill bit that will create the shape they are striving for.

1. The castle will need several turrets, which are made by pouring chocolate into a mold that will form a cone.

   a. Which of the figures shown is a cone?

   Fig. 1   Fig. 2   Fig. 3   Fig. 4

   b. Which of the drill bits shown will form a cone after being rotated in a plastic molding compound?

   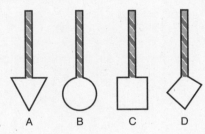

   A   B   C   D

c. What is the shape on the drill bit that forms the cone in the mold as it is being rotated?

d. If the triangle on the drill bit is 2 inches wide and 1 inch tall, what will the dimensions of the cone be that is formed by the rotation of the bit?

2. The castle that the company is making is going to have long circular columns in the front.

a. What type of solid mold is needed to create circular columns?

b. Which of the drill bits shown will form the mold needed after being rotated in the plastic molding compound?

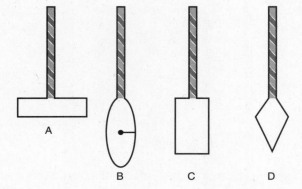

c. What is the shape of the drill bit that will create the column mold?

d. If the width of the shape on the end of the drill bit being rotated is 3 inches, what is the radius of the base of the cylinder going to be?

Name _____ Date _____

3. To complete the castle, the company is going to create small cannonballs for the cannon that will be situated on the roof of the castle.

   a. What type of solid mold is needed to make cannonballs?

   b. Which of the drill bits shown will form the mold needed if the cannonballs will have a radius of 0.25 inch?

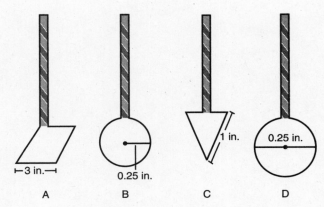

A   B   C   D

   c. What is the shape of the drill bit that will create the cannonball mold?

Name _____ Date _____

Cakes and Pancakes
Translating and Stacking Two-Dimensional Figures

Theodore is starting a new company that will manufacture food storage containers. He asks his engineers to design several different containers based on which type of containers will sell the best.

1. The end of one container is a rectangle

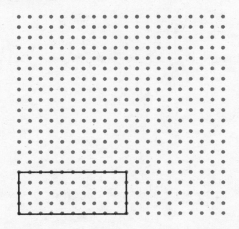

a. Translate the rectangle in a diagonal direction to create a second rectangle.

b. Use dashed line segments to connect each pair of corresponding vertices in the rectangles.

c. What do you notice about the relationship among the line segments in your drawing?

d. What is the name of the solid formed by this translation?

2. The base of one container is a triangle.

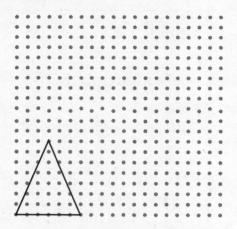

    a. Translate the triangle in a diagonal direction to create a second triangle.

    b. Use dashed line segments to connect each pair of corresponding vertices in the triangles.

    c. What do you notice about the relationship among the line segments in your drawing?

    d. What is the name of the solid formed by this translation?

Name _____ Date _____

3. Theodore gets a contract from a restaurant to make containers for their soup. The bottom of the container is a disc. An oval is drawn to represent what the base of the container might look like.

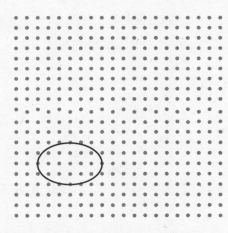

a. Translate the oval in a diagonal direction to create a second oval.

b. Use dashed line segments to connect the tops and the bottoms of the ovals.

c. What do you notice about the relationship between the line segments in your drawing?

d. What is the name of the solid formed by this translation?

The Harrington Heights Middle School is getting ready for its spring musical. The students in the art classes are using donated cardboard boxes to make the props.

4. One of the props for the show needs to be a suitcase. The directors want its weight to be light because it is used in one scene to playfully hit another actor. The art students decide to make the suitcase shape by stacking rectangles of the same shape and size on top of each other. Each cardboard cutout is 48 inches long by 30 inches wide.

   a. The students are going to stack 4 rectangular cutouts on top of each other. What is the name of the solid formed by this stack of rectangles?

   b. If the thickness of each cardboard rectangle is 0.25 inch, what is the thickness of the suitcase?

   c. Relate the dimensions of the suitcase formed to the dimensions of the rectangles.

   d. The directors of the show have decided that they would like the suitcase to have a greater thickness than 1 inch. They would like it to have a thickness of 3 inches. How many rectangles do the students need to stack?

Name _____ Date _____

5. The art students need to work on making a stop sign for the show using stacks of figures that have similar shapes and sizes.

   a. What type of shape will they need to cut out from the cardboard for their stack?

   b. What is the name of the solid that will be formed by this stack?

   c. The cardboard the students use for the stop sign is 0.125 inch thick. If the directors want the stop sign to be 1 inch thick, how many stop signs will the students need to stack?

6. One of the scenes of the musical involves a scene on city streets. The director would like to have several traffic cones set up for the scene.

   a. The students need to build up each cone using stacks of shapes. What type of shapes will they use? What should the size of the shapes be?

   b. What is the relationship among the discs getting stacked?

   c. The cardboard they are using for the cone is 0.5 inch thick. The directors want the traffic cones to be 14 inches tall. How many discs will the students need to stack for each cone?

Name _____ Date _____

Cavalieri's Principles
Application of Cavalieri's Principles

1. Divide the figure shown into approximately 10 rectangles. What is the length, the height, and the area of each rectangle?

2. What is the approximate area of the irregularly shaped figure?

3. If this irregularly shaped figure were divided into 1000 congruent rectangles, what would be the approximate area of the figure?

4. If this irregularly shaped figure were divided into *n* congruent rectangles, what would be the approximate area of the figure?

The Leaning Tower of Pisa in Italy is about 180 feet tall from the top of the tower vertically to the ground. It has a diameter of approximately 51 feet.

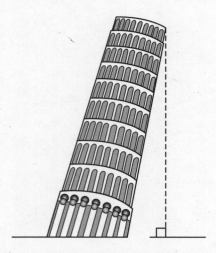

5. Determine the approximate volume of the tower. Explain your reasoning.

Name _____ Date _____

Spin to Win
Volume of Cones and Pyramids

1. Joel owns a frozen yogurt and fruit smoothie shop. He just placed an order for three different sizes of cones. He needs to determine how much to charge for each cone and decides that knowing the volume of each might help him make his decision.

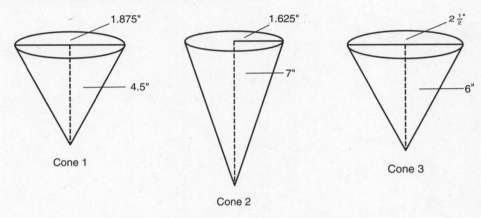

Cone 1

Cone 2

Cone 3

   a. Which cone do you think has the greatest volume? Explain your reasoning.

   b. Identify the radius, the diameter, and he height of cone 1. How did you determine the radius of the cone?

c. Calculate the volume of cone 1. Show your work. Round your answer to the nearest hundredth.

4

d. Identify the radius, the diameter, and the height of cone 2. How did you determine the diameter of the cone?

e. Calculate the volume of Cone 2. Show your work. Round to the nearest hundredth.

Name _____ Date _____

f. Identify the radius, the diameter, and the height of cone 3. How did you determine the radius of the cone?

g. Calculate the volume of Cone 3. Show your work. Round to the nearest hundredth.

h. Determine which size cone Joel should charge the most for and the least for. Explain your reasoning.

i. Compare the volumes of all three cones.

2. Pyramid tents were popular for a time during the 19th century. Although their popularity declined during the 20th century, they have recently begun to regain popularity again. The design is ideal for shaping canvas, and it only requires one pole and some stakes to secure it. Joe wants to make a right square pyramid tent and is considering two different sizes. He will either make one with a base that is 10 feet by 10 feet and has a height of 12 feet, or he will make one with a base that is 12 feet by 12 feet and has a height of 8 feet.

   a. Sketch the two pyramid designs Joe is considering and label them with the given measurements.

 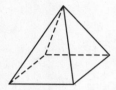

   b. How can you determine which pyramid tent will have the most interior space?

   c. Calculate the volume of each proposed pyramid tent. Show your work.

   d. Which tent would you recommend Joe make? Explain your reasoning.

Name _____ Date _____

Spheres à la Archimedes
Volume of a Sphere

Calculate the volume of each sphere. Use 3.14 for π and round to the nearest tenth, if necessary.

1.

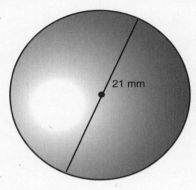

21 mm

2.

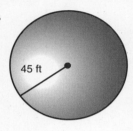

45 ft

3. A can holds 3 tennis balls as shown in the figure. The radius of each tennis ball is 3 centimeters.

   a. What is the volume of a single tennis ball?

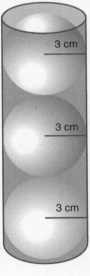

3 cm

3 cm

3 cm

   b. What is the total volume all 3 tennis balls take up?

c. Can you determine the height of the can? Explain your reasoning.

d. What is the volume of the can? Use 3.14 for π.

e. What is the volume of the can not taken up by the tennis balls?

Name _____ Date _____

Turn Up the . . .
Using Volume Formulas

1. The Luxor Hotel in Las Vegas is a replica of the Pyramid of Khafre at Giza, one of the seven wonders of the world. The Luxor's base is a square with a side length of 646 feet, and it is 350 feet tall.

   a. What is the volume of the Luxor Hotel?

   b. The Pyramid of Khafre has a volume of 2,226,450 cubic meters. Its base is a square with a side length of 215 meters. What is the height of the Pyramid of Khafre?

2. A store sells square pyramid-shaped scented candles. The dimensions of two of the candles are shown.

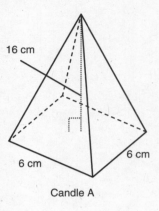

16 cm

6 cm

6 cm

Candle A

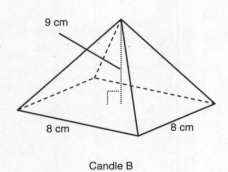

9 cm

8 cm

8 cm

Candle B

a. Calculate the volume of each candle.

b. Both candles are made of wax. Which candle contains more wax? Explain.

Name _____ Date _____

3. Your municipality is replacing the storage tanks in the community. Which plan provides the greater total capacity?

Plan 1: Install one cylindrical tank that is 150 feet tall and has a radius of 50 feet.

Plan 2: Install two cylindrical tanks that are 75 feet tall. One cylindrical tank has a radius of 30 feet, and one tank has a radius of 25 feet.

Use 3.14 for π and round your answers to the nearest tenth if necessary.

4. A traffic cone has a radius of 9 inches and a height of 30 inches. What is the volume of this traffic cone?

5. A funnel that is used to change the oil in a car is in the shape of a cone. The base of the funnel has a circumference of 60 centimeters. The height of the funnel is 25 centimeters. How much oil will this funnel hold?

6. Today's deal at the ice cream shop is a mini cone with one scoop of ice cream.

   a. A mini ice cream cone has a diameter of 3.5 centimeters and a height of 6 centimeters. How much ice cream fits in the cone?

   b. One scoop of ice cream has the same diameter as the cone, 3.5 centimeters. What's the volume of 1 scoop of ice cream?

Name _____ Date _____

Tree Rings
Cross Sections

Describe the shape of each cross section.

1.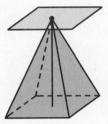

2.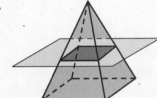

3.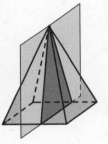

4.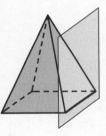

5.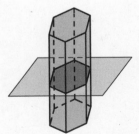

6.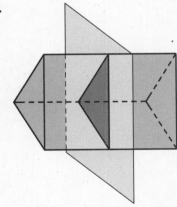

7. Sketch two cross sections of a pentagonal prism—one cross section that is parallel to the base and another cross section that is perpendicular to the base.

8. Sketch two cross sections of a cone—one cross section that is parallel to the base and another cross section that is perpendicular to the base.

4

9. A solid's cross section parallel to the base is an octagon. A cross section of the solid perpendicular to the base is a triangle. Identify the solid.

10. A solid's cross section parallel to the base is a triangle. A cross section of the solid perpendicular to the base is a rectangle. Identify the solid.

Name _____ Date _____

Two Dimensions Meet Three Dimensions
Diagonals in Three Dimensions

1. What is the length of a three-dimensional diagonal of the rectangular prism?

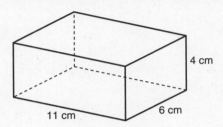

4 cm

11 cm   6 cm

2. What is the length of a three-dimensional diagonal of the rectangular prism?

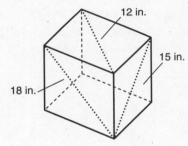

12 in.

15 in.

18 in.

3. A rectangular box has a length of 6 feet and a width of 2 feet. The length of a three-dimensional diagonal of the box is 7 feet. What is the height of the box?

4. The length of the diagonal across the front of a rectangular box is 20 inches, and the length of the diagonal across the side of the box is 15 inches. The length of a three-dimensional diagonal of the box is 23 inches. What is the length of a three-dimensional diagonal of the box?

5. Pablo is packing for a business trip. He is almost finished packing when he realizes that he forgot to pack his umbrella. Before Pablo takes the time to repack his suitcase, he wants to know if the umbrella will fit in the suitcase. His suitcase is in the shape of a rectangular prism and has a length of 2 feet, a width of 1.5 feet, and a height of 0.75 foot. The umbrella is 30 inches long. Will the umbrella fit in Pablo's suitcase? Explain your reasoning.

Name _____ Date _____

Name That Triangle!
Classifying Triangles on the Coordinate Plane

1. The grid shown is a map of Stoneville and the locations of several businesses in the town. A line segment has been drawn between the locations of the mall and the diner. Using this line segment as one side of a triangle, determine the business (or businesses) whose location, when connected with the line segment, would result in each of the following types of triangles.

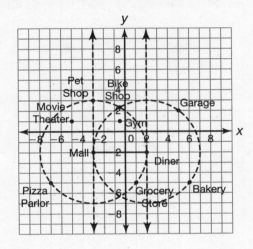

   a. an isosceles triangle

   b. an acute triangle

   c. a scalene triangle

   d. a right triangle

e. an equilateral triangle

f. a obtuse triangle

2. The grid shown represents a map of Jose's neighborhood. It shows the locations of his house as well as the houses of four friends.

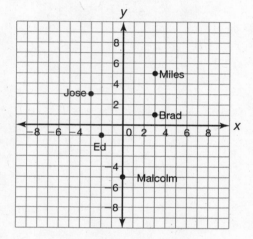

a. Draw a triangle between the houses of Jose, Ed, and Brad. Determine if this triangle is a scalene, an isosceles, or an equilateral triangle. Explain your reasoning.

Name _____ Date _____

b. Determine if the triangle is a right triangle. Explain your reasoning. If it is not a right triangle, use a protractor to determine what type of triangle it is.

c. Jose, Miles, and Brad are meeting for band rehearsal. Miles claims that the distance from Jose's house to his house is the same as the distance from Jose's house to Brad's house. Is his claim correct? Explain your answer. What kind of triangle is formed if you connect all their houses in the shape of a triangle?

d. A new boy, James, moved into the neighborhood at the location (−3, −5). Plot and label James's house on the grid. Then, determine if the triangle formed by connecting his house, Jose's house, and Malcolm's house is a right triangle.

5

Name _____ Date _____

Inside Out
Triangle Sum, Exterior Angle, and Exterior Angle Inequality Theorems

1. Determine the measure of angle *UPM* in the figure shown. Explain your reasoning and show all your work.

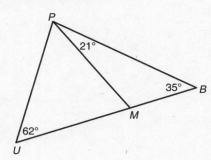

2. In the figure shown, $\overrightarrow{AB}$ is parallel to $\overrightarrow{DE}$. Determine the measure of each missing angle in the figure.

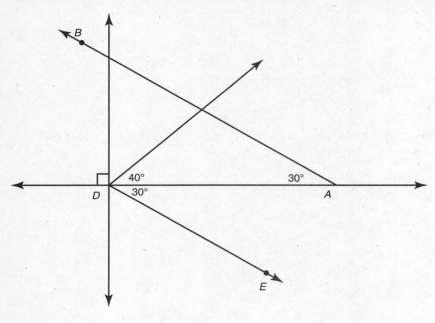

3. You are building a triangular play area for your new puppy. You decide that the play area will have angle measures of 50° and 40° as shown.

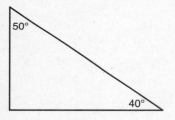

a. Which side of the play area is the longest?

b. Which side of the play area is the shortest?

Name _____ Date _____

c. Explain how you determined your answers in parts (a) and (b).

Solve for *x*.

4.
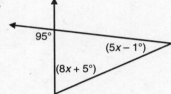

5.
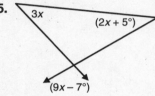

6. Use the figure shown to write a paragraph proof of the Exterior Angle Inequality Theorem.

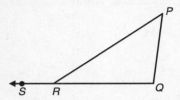

Given: Triangle *PQR* with exterior angle *PRS*

Prove: $m\angle PRS > m\angle P$ and $m\angle PRS > m\angle Q$

Name _____ Date _____

Trade Routes and Pasta, Anyone?
The Triangle Inequality Theorem

1. You are building a triangular pen for baby ducks. The sides of the pen will be made from lumber you have left from other projects. You have two 12-foot boards, one 14-foot board, one 8-foot board, one 4-foot board, one 3-foot board, and one 2-foot board. Use this information to answer parts (a) through (f).

   a. Suppose you choose the 14-foot board and the 4-foot board. Of the boards you have left over, what is the longest board that can be used for the third side of the pen? Explain.

   b. Suppose you choose a 12-foot board and the 8-foot board. Of the boards you have left over, what is the shortest board that can be used for the third side of the pen? Explain.

   c. Suppose you choose a 12-foot board and the 4-foot board. Of the boards you have left over, which board(s) can be used for the third side of the pen? Explain.

d. How many different triangular pens can be formed using the 4-foot board?
List the side lengths of each possible triangular pen.

e. If you only have three boards and their lengths are 5 feet, 8 feet, and 4 feet, can you
form a triangular pen? Explain.

f. Suppose you decide to build a pen with side lengths of 14 feet, 12 feet, and 8 feet as
shown. Which angle has the greatest measure? Which angle has the least measure? Explain.

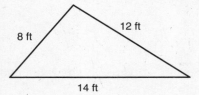

List the angles and sides of each triangle in order from least to greatest.
Do not measure the angles or sides.

2.

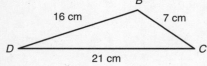

Name _____ Date _____

3.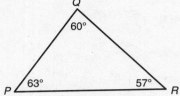

4. Triangle *ABC* with the following: $m\angle A = 27°$, $m\angle B = 119°$, and $m\angle C = 34°$

5. Triangle *RST* with the following: RS = 8 centimeters, ST = 20 centimeters, and RT = 14 centimeters

Determine whether it is possible to form a triangle using segments with the following measurements. Explain.

6. 14 inches, 21 inches, 7 inches

7. 26 feet, 10 feet, 18 feet

8. 2.2 millimeters, 7.2 millimeters, 5.1 millimeters

Name _____ Date _____

Stamps Around the World
Properties of a 45°–45°–90° Triangle

1. The legs of the isosceles triangle each measure 14 inches.
Calculate the length of the hypotenuse.

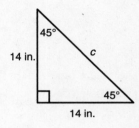

2. Calculate the value of c.

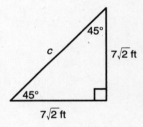

3. The perimeter of the square is 32 centimeters.
Calculate the length of its diagonal.

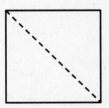

4. Calculate the value of a.

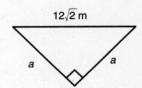

5. The length of a diagonal of the square is 36 centimeters. Calculate the length of each side.

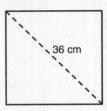

6. The length of a diagonal of the square is 12 centimeters. Calculate the area.

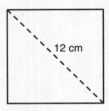

7. Calculate the area of the figure shown using the information given. The figure is composed of a triangle and a semicircle. Use 3.14 for π.

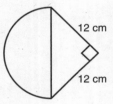

8. The length of a diagonal of the square in the figure shown is 60 inches. Calculate the perimeter of the figure. The figure is composed of a square and a semicircle.

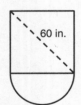

Name _____ Date _____

More Stamps, Really?
Properties of a 30°–60°–90° Triangle

1. The length of the hypotenuse in the 30°–60°–90°
triangle shown is 28 meters. Calculate the lengths of
sides *a* and *b*.

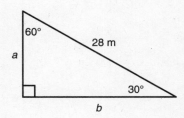

2. The length of the side opposite the 30-degree angle is 5 feet.
Calculate the lengths of sides *b* and *c*.

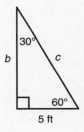

3. The length of the side opposite the 60-degree angle is
8 millimeters. Calculate the lengths of sides *a* and *c*.

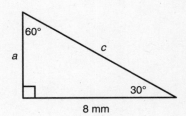

4. A broadcast antenna is situated on top of a tower. The signal travels from the antenna to your house so you can watch TV. The angle of elevation from your house to the tower measures 30 degrees, and the distance from your house to the tower is 500 feet. Calculate the height of the tower and the distance the signal travels.

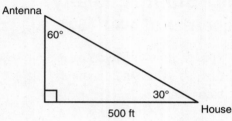

5. The length of the longer leg in the 30°−60°−90° triangle shown is 22 miles. Calculate the length of the hypotenuse.

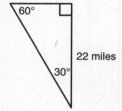

6. The length of the shorter leg in the 30°−60°−90° triangle shown is 13 meters. Calculate the length of the hypotenuse.

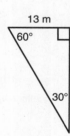

Name _____ Date _____

7. Calculate the perimeter of the trapezoid.

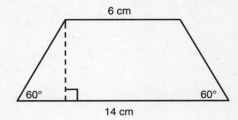

8. Calculate the area of the triangle.

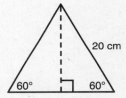

9. Calculate the area of the trapezoid.

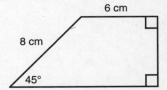

10. A broadcast antenna is situated on top of a tower, and the signal travels from the antenna
to your house so that you can watch TV. The angle of elevation from your house to the tower
measures 30 degrees, and the distance from your house to the tower is 775 feet. Calculate the height
of the tower and the distance the signal travels.

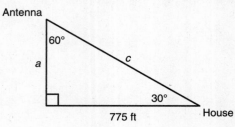

Name _____ Date _____

Big and Small
Dilating Triangles to Create Similar Triangles

1. Use quadrilateral *ABCD* shown on the grid to complete part (a) through part (c).

   a. On the grid, draw the image of quadrilateral *ABCD* dilated using a scale factor of 3 with the center of dilation at the origin. Label the image *JKLM*.

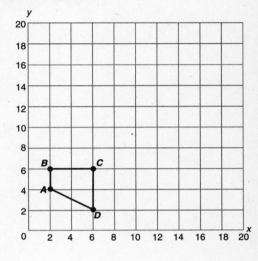

   b. On the grid, draw the image of quadrilateral *ABCD* dilated using a scale factor of 0.5 with the center of dilation at the origin. Label the image *WXYZ*.

   c. Identify the coordinates of the vertices of quadrilaterals *JKLM* and *WXYZ*.

2. The vertices of triangle *ABC* are *A*(−6, 15), *B*(0, 5), and *C*(3, 10). Without drawing the figure, determine the coordinates of the vertices of the image of triangle *ABC* dilated using a scale factor of $\frac{1}{3}$ with the center of dilation at the origin. Explain your reasoning.

6

3. The vertices of trapezoid *WXYZ* are *W*(−1, 2), *X*(−3, −1), *Y*(5, −1), and *Z*(3, 2). Without drawing the figure, determine the coordinates of the vertices of the image of trapezoid *WXYZ* dilated using a scale factor of 5 with the center of dilation at the origin. Explain your reasoning.

4. The vertices of hexagon *PQRSTV* are *P*(−5, 0), *Q*(−5, 5), *R*(0, 7), *S*(5, 2), *T*(5, −2), and *V*(0, −5). Without drawing the figure, determine the coordinates of the vertices of the image of hexagon *PQRSTV* dilated about the origin using a scale factor of 4.2. Explain your reasoning.

5. Triangle *A′B′C′* is a dilation of △*ABC* with the center of dilation at the origin. List the coordinates of the vertices of △*ABC* and △*A′B′C′*. What is the scale factor of the dilation? Explain.

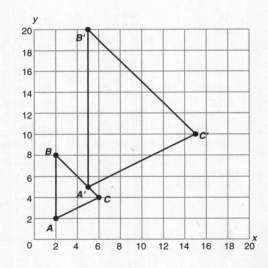

6

Name _____ Date _____

6. On the grid, draw the image of quadrilateral *QRST* using the dilation $(x, y) \rightarrow (0.75x, 0.75y)$. Label the image *Q′R′S′T′*.

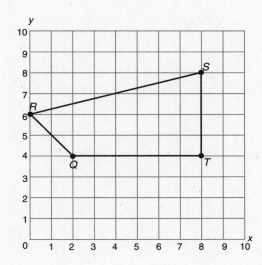

6

Name _____ Date _____

Similar Triangles or Not?
Similar Triangle Theorems

1. In the figure below, $\overleftrightarrow{NS} \parallel \overleftrightarrow{BE}$. Use the information given in the figure to determine the $m\angle SNA$, $m\angle NAS$, $m\angle ABE$, and $m\angle BAE$. Is $\triangle NSA$ similar to $\triangle EBA$? If the triangles are similar, write a similarity statement. Use complete sentences to explain your answers.

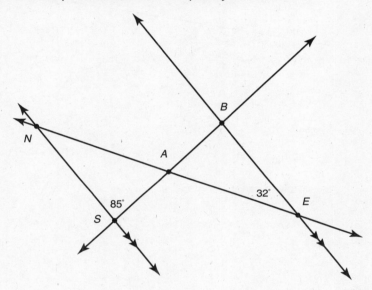

2. Use a ruler to determine whether the triangles shown are similar. Explain your answer.

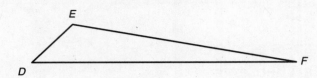
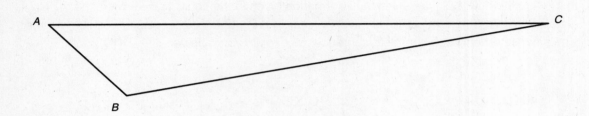

Name _____ Date _____

3. In the figure shown, $\overline{NU} \parallel \overline{CV}$. Use the figure to complete part (a) through part (c).

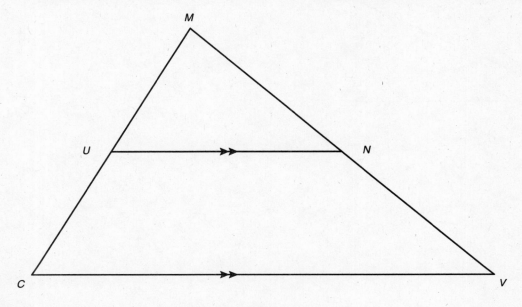

a. Is $\angle MUN \cong \angle MCV$? Explain your answer.

b. Is $\angle MNU \cong \angle MVC$? Explain your answer.

c. Is $\triangle CMV \sim \triangle UMN$? Explain your answer.

4. In the figure shown, segments *AB* and *DE* are parallel. The length of segment *BC* is 10 units and the length of segment *CD* is 5 units. Use this information to calculate the value of *x*. Explain how you determined your answer.

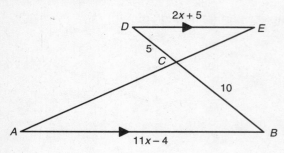

Name _____ Date _____

Keep It in Proportion
Theorems About Proportionality

Calculate the indicated length in each figure.

1. $\overline{KN}$ bisects $\angle K$. Calculate *MN*.

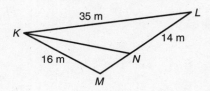

2. $\overline{SQ}$ bisects $\angle S$. Calculate *SR*.

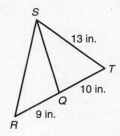

3. Use the figure and the given information to write a paragraph proof of the Angle Bisector/Proportional Side Theorem.

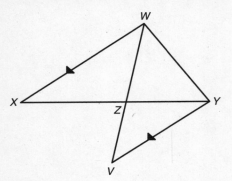

Given: $\overline{WZ}$ bisects $\angle XWY$ and $\overline{XW} \parallel \overline{VY}$

Prove: $\dfrac{WX}{XZ} = \dfrac{WY}{YZ}$

Name _____ Date _____

4. The figure shows a truss on a bridge. Segment *BF* bisects angle *CBE*. Use this information to calculate *EF* and *CF*.

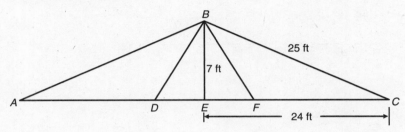

5. The figure shows a truss for a barn roof. Segment *DF* bisects angle *ADB* and segment *EG* bisects angle *CEB*. Triangle *DBE* is an equilateral triangle. Use this information to calculate the perimeter of the truss.

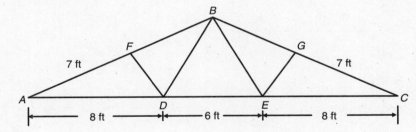

6. Given: $\overline{AB} \parallel \overline{CE}$

Calculate the value of x.

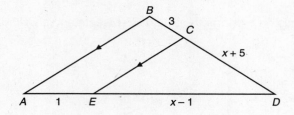

7. Calculate a value for x such that $\overline{AB} \parallel \overline{CE}$.

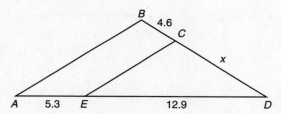

Name _____ Date _____

8. Given: $L_1 \parallel L_2 \parallel L_3$

Calculate *HI*.

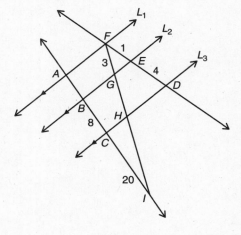

9. In $\triangle XYZ$, the midpoint of $\overline{XY}$ is $A(-3, 0.5)$, the midpoint of $\overline{XZ}$ is $B(1, -6)$, and the midpoint of $\overline{YZ}$ is $C(3, 0.5)$. Use the Triangle Midsegment Theorem to determine the coordinates of the vertices of $\triangle XYZ$. Show all of your work and graph triangles *ABC* and *XYZ* on the grid.

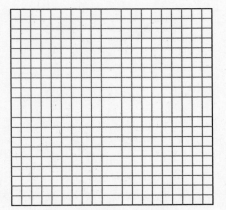

Name _____ Date _____

Geometric Mean
More Similar Triangles

Solve for *x*.

1.

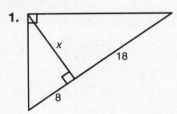

2.

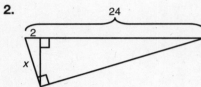

3. Use the figure and the given information to write a paragraph proof of the Right Triangle/Altitude Similarity Theorem.

   Given: Triangle *ABC* is a right triangle with altitude *CD*.

   Prove: △*ABC* ~ △*ACD* ~ △*CBD*

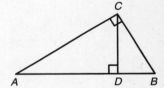

6

4. The geometric mean of two numbers is 20. One of the numbers is 50. What is the other number?

5. The geometric mean of two numbers is $5\sqrt{3}$. One of the numbers is 3. What is the other number?

6. Use the figure and the given information to prove the Right Triangle Altitude Theorem 1.

   Given: Triangle *ABC* is a right triangle with altitude *CD*.

   Prove: $\dfrac{AD}{CD} = \dfrac{CD}{BD}$

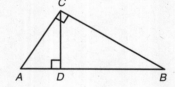

6

Name _____ Date _____

7. Use the figure and the given information to prove the Right Triangle Altitude/Leg Theorem

Given: Triangle *ABC* is a right triangle with altitude *CD*.

Prove: $\dfrac{AB}{AC} = \dfrac{AC}{AD}$ and $\dfrac{AB}{BC} = \dfrac{BC}{BD}$

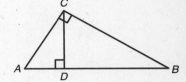

Solve for *a*, *b*, and *c*.

8.

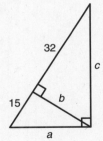

6

9.

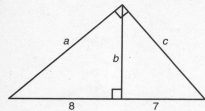

10. You are standing 15 feet from a tree. Your line of sight to the top of the tree and to the bottom of the tree forms a 90-degree angle as shown in the diagram. The distance between your line of sight and the ground is 5 feet. Estimate the height of the tree.

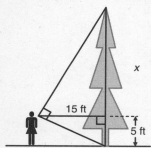

Name _____ Date _____

Proving the Pythagorean Theorem
Proving the Pythagorean Theorem and the Converse of the Pythagorean Theorem

1. Use this figure to prove the Pythagorean Theorem. Given that the bottom triangle is a right triangle, this figure is constructed by making three copies of the bottom triangle, as shown.

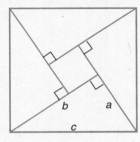

   a. Determine the area of the large square.

   b. Determine the area of the small square.

   c. Determine the total area of the four triangles.

   d. Show that the area of the large square is equal to the sum of the area of the four triangles and the small square.

2. In order to prove the Pythagorean Theorem using this figure, show that the sum of the three triangles is equal to the area of the trapezoid. (Note: $A_{trapezoid} = h\left(\dfrac{b_1 + b_2}{2}\right)$ where h is the height and b is the base.)

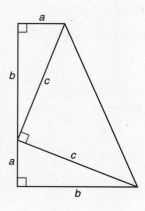

Name _____ Date _____

3. Consider the figure where $a^2 + b^2 = c^2$.

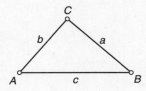

In order to prove the Converse of the Pythagorean Theorem, Peter constructs a new triangle with the same leg lengths of *a* and *b*, and makes angle *G* a right angle.

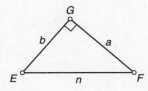

Complete the statements in the two column proof to prove the Converse of the Pythagorean Theorem, that traingle *ABC* is a right triangle.

Reason	Statement
$a^2 + b^2 = n^2$	
$a^2 + b^2 = c^2$	
	Transitive Property
$\triangle ABC \cong \triangle EFG$	
$\angle c = 90°$	
$\triangle ABC$ is a right triangle	

6

Name _____ Date _____

Indirect Measurement
Application of Similar Triangles

1. You want to measure the height of a tree at the community park. You stand in the tree's shadow so that the tip of your shadow meets the tip of the tree's shadow on the ground, 2 meters from where you are standing. The distance from the tree to the tip of the tree's shadow is 5.4 meters. You are 1.25 meters tall. Draw a diagram to represent the situation. Then, calculate the height of the tree.

2. You and a friend are on the 10th floor of apartment buildings that are directly across the street from each other, and have balconies. The two of you are making a banner to hang between the apartment buildings. The banner must cross the street. To hang the banner, you and your friend need to attach it to hooks on the wall of each balcony. The wall of your balcony is 6 feet away from the street and the wall of your friend's balcony is 4 feet away from the street. You also know that your friend's balcony is 10 feet away from the end of his building and your balcony is 100 feet away from the edge of your building. How wide is the street between you and your friend's apartment buildings? How long does the banner need to be? Show all your work and use complete sentences in your answer.

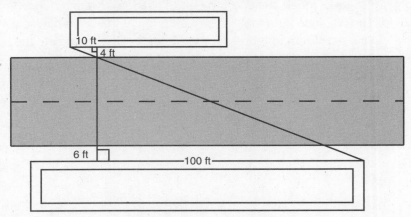

Name _____ Date _____

Slide, Flip, Turn: The Latest Dance Craze?
Translating, Rotating, and Reflecting Geometric Figures

1. Transform rectangle *JKLM* so it sits in the shaded rectangle in Quadrant III.

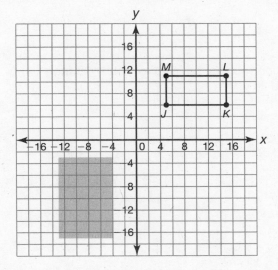

a. How many different transformations will it take to place rectangle *JKLM* in the shaded area in Quadrant III?

b. Describe and perform a transformation to move rectangle *JKLM* to Quadrant II. Identify the coordinates of the vertices of the transformed rectangle, *J′K′L′M′*. Explain how you determined your answer.

c. Describe and perform the transformation that can be used to move rectangle *J′K′L′M′* to Quadrant III. Identify the coordinates of the vertices of the transformed rectangle, *J″K″L″M″*. Explain how you determined your answer.

d. Could a different transformation(s) be used to move rectangle *JKLM* to Quadrant III? Explain your reasoning.

2. Consider figure *QRST*.

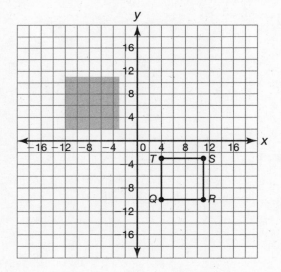

Ramona states that there are three ways to transform *QRST* to place its image in the shaded area in Quadrant II.

- Translate *QRST* vertically 13 units up, then horizontally 15 units to the left.
- Reflect *QRST* over the *x*-axis then over the *y*-axis.
- Rotate *QRST* 180° counterclockwise (or clockwise) about the origin.

7

Name _____ Date _____

a. Without graphing, determine the coordinates of the vertices of the image for each of the transformations Ramona listed. Explain how you determined your answers.

b. Which transformation would you recommend that Ramona choose? Explain your reasoning.

c. Perform the transformation you chose in part (b).

7

Name _____ Date _____

All the Same to You
Congruent Triangles

1. Analyze triangle *ABC*.

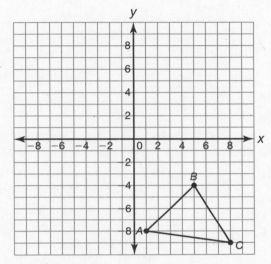

a. Describe a transformation that can be performed on △*ABC* that will result in a triangle being created in Quadrant I.

b. Will the transformation you described preserve the size and shape of the triangle? Explain your reasoning.

c. Perform the transformation and name the new triangle *DEF*.

d. List the coordinates for the vertices of both triangles.

e. Using the names of the vertices, write a triangle congruence statement for the triangles.

f. Using your congruence statement, identify the congruent angles.

g. Using your congruence statement, identify the congruent sides.

2. Analyze triangle *MNO*.

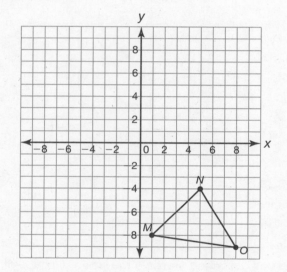

a. Describe a transformation that can be performed on △ *MNO* that will result in a triangle being created in Quadrant III.

b. Will the transformation you described preserve the size and shape of the triangle?

c. Perform the transformation and name the new triangle *PQR*.

Name _____ Date _____

   d. List the coordinates for the vertices of both triangles.

   e. Using the names of the vertices, write a triangle congruence statement for the triangles.

   f. Using your congruence statement, identify the congruent angles.

   g. Using your congruence statement, identify the congruent sides.

7

Name _____ Date _____

Side-Side-Side
Side-Side-Side Congruence Theorem

1. Analyze the triangles shown.

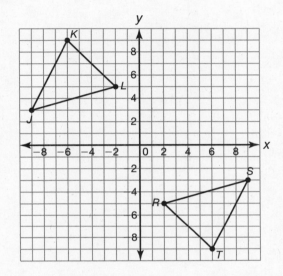

a. Are the two triangles shown on the grid congruent? Show and explain how you determined your answer.

b. Juan says the triangle congruency statement for these triangles should be $\triangle JKL \cong \triangle RST$. Natsu says the triangle congruency statement for these triangles should be $\triangle JKL \cong \triangle SRT$. Who is correct? Explain your reasoning.

Name _____ Date _____

Side-Angle-Side
Side-Angle-Side Congruence Theorem

1. Analyze the triangles shown.

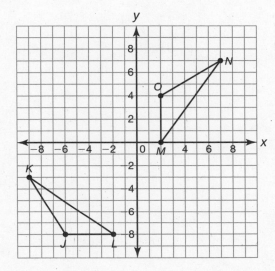

a. Use the distance formula and a protractor to prove that the two triangles shown on the grid are congruent by SAS. Show your work.

7

b. Mark the triangles to show which sides and angles are congruent.

c. Write a congruency statement for the triangles.

7

Name _____ Date _____

You Shouldn't Make Assumptions
Angle-Side-Angle Congruence Theorem

1. Emerson wants to translate △ABC and then reflect it over the *y*-axis to form a new triangle in Quadrant II. She uses what she knows about transformations to determine the vertices of △A′B′C′ before performing the transformations.

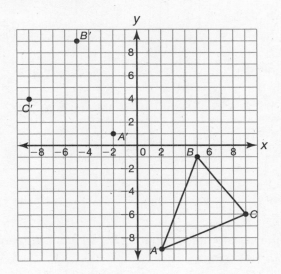

a. Briefly describe how Emerson can use the ASA Congruence Theorem to determine whether or not she transformed △ABC, such that the image is congruent to the pre-image.

b. Connect points A′, B′, and C′. Use a protractor to determine the measure of two corresponding angles in each triangle.

c. Calculate the length of the included side of △*ABC* and △*A′B′C′*. Show your work.

d. Did Emerson perform the transformations on △*ABC* so that the image is congruent to the pre-image? Explain your reasoning.

Name _____ Date _____

Ahhhhh . . . We're Sorry We Didn't Include You!
Angle-Angle-Side Congruence Theorem

1. Describe and use AAS to prove that triangle *LMN* is congruent to triangle *QRS*.

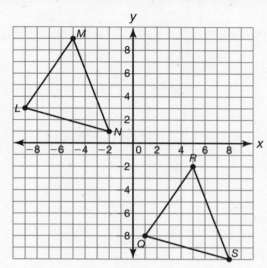

2. Triangles *ABC* and *DFG* are given.

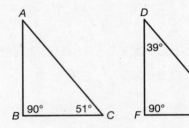

a. Side *BC* of △*ABC* is congruent to side *FG* of △*DFG*. Mark the triangles to show that these sides are congruent.

b. Do you have enough information to determine whether △*ABD* is congruent to △*DFG*? Explain your reasoning.

c. Without using a protractor, calculate the measure of ∠*BAC*. Show your work. Write the measure on the triangle.

d. Now, do you have enough information to determine that △*ABC* is congruent to △*DFG*? Write congruence statements to justify your reasoning.

7

Name _____ Date _____

Congruent Triangles in Action
Using Congruent Triangles

1. Use triangle congruency proofs to prove the statement using the given information.

a.

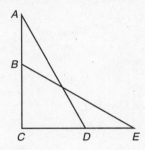

Given: $\angle A \cong \angle E$

$\overline{AB} \cong \overline{EC}$

Prove: $\overline{CB} \cong \overline{DC}$

b.

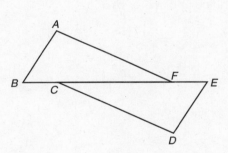

Given: $\overline{FE} \cong \overline{BC}$

$\overline{AF} \parallel \overline{CD}, \overline{AB} \parallel \overline{ED}$

Prove: $\triangle ABF \cong \triangle DEC$

c.

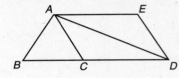

Given: △ABC is equilateral

$\overline{AC} \parallel \overline{ED}$

$\overline{AB} \cong \overline{ED}$

Prove: ∠E ≅ ∠ACD

d.

Given: $\overline{AD}$ is a perpendicular bisector of $\overline{BC}$

$\overline{AB} \cong \overline{AC}$

Prove: △ABD ≅ △ACD

7

Name _____ Date _____

e.

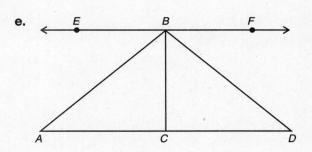

Given: $\overleftrightarrow{EF} \parallel \overline{AD}$

$\overline{BC}$ is angle bisector of $\angle ABD$

$\overline{BC}$ is the perpendicular bisector of $\overleftrightarrow{EF}$

Prove: $\triangle CAB \cong \triangle CDB$

2. Write the information needed in each situation to prove that the triangles are congruent, and state the postulate, or state that there is already enough information to prove the specified triangles congruent, and state the postulate.

a.

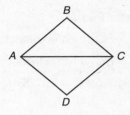

Given: $\angle B \cong \angle D$

Prove: $\triangle ABC \cong \triangle ADC$

b.

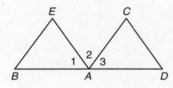

Given: $\angle BAC \cong \angle DAE$

$\overline{AE} \cong \overline{AC}$

A is the midpoint of $\overline{BD}$

Prove: $\triangle BEA \cong \triangle DCA$

c.

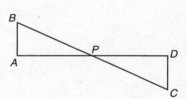

Given: $\angle A$ and $\angle D$ are right angles

Prove: $\triangle BAP \cong \triangle CDP$

7

Name _____ Date _____

Time to Get Right
Right Triangle Congruence Theorems

Write a Given statement and state the theorem that proves the triangles are congruent. Then, write a congruence statement.

1.

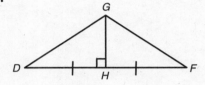

2.

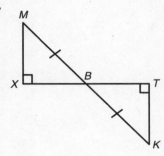

Determine the information that is needed to use the indicated theorem to show that the triangles are congruent.

3. △RQW ≅ △RPW by HL

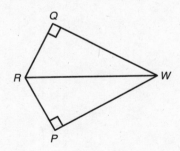

4. △JNZ ≅ △HNC by LA

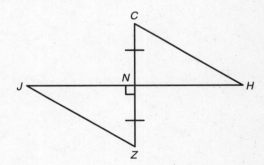

5. In the following figure triangle *ABD* is an isosceles triangle, and $\overline{AC}$ is perpendicular to $\overline{BD}$. Use a two-column proof to show that $\angle B \cong \angle D$.

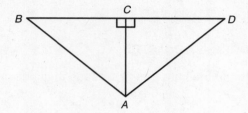

Name _____ Date _____

CPCTC
Corresponding Parts of Congruent Triangles are Congruent

1. What is the width of the swimming pool? Explain how you got your answer.

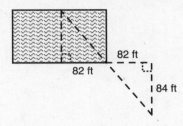

2. Marcel is painting the triangular section of a shuffleboard court shown in the figure. He starts by putting 41 feet of tape around the outside of the triangle. He knows that the base of the triangle is 16 feet and each base angle of the triangle measures 50 degrees. What is the length of each leg?

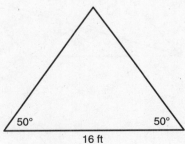

© Carnegie Learning

Calculate the measure of angle 1. Show your work.

3.

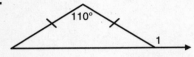

4.

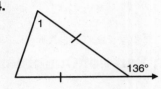

5. Use a two-column proof to show that $\overline{LM}$ bisects $\overline{DF}$.

     Given: $\overline{LF} \parallel \overline{DM}, \overline{DL} \parallel \overline{MF}$

     Prove: $\overline{LM}$ bisects $\overline{DF}$

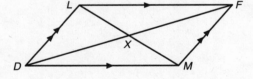

Name _____ Date _____

Congruence Theorems in Action
Isosceles Triangle Theorems

1. Use the Isosceles Triangle Perpendicular Bisector Theorem to make a statement about isosceles △CYX.

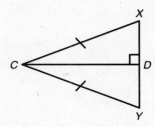

2. Use the Triangle Base Theorem to make a statement about isosceles △PBD.

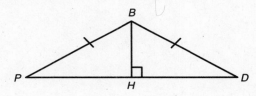

3. Use the Isosceles Triangle Angle Bisector to Congruent Sides Theorem to make a statement about isosceles △KSF.

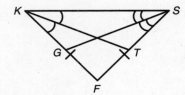

Solve for *x*.

4.

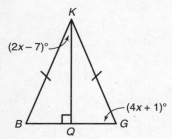

5.

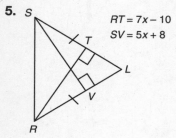

$RT = 7x - 10$
$SV = 5x + 8$

6.

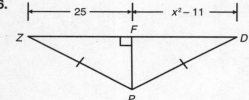

Name _____ Date _____

7. Use a flow chart proof to show that segment *AY* is congruent to segment *CZ*.

Given: $\overline{AB} \cong \overline{CB}$, $\angle AXY \cong \angle CXZ$, $AX = CX$

Prove: $\overline{AY} \cong \overline{CZ}$

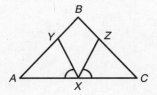

Name _____ Date _____

Making Some Assumptions
Inverse, Contrapositive, Direct Proof, and Indirect Proof

1. Consider the conditional statement "If a quadrilateral is a rectangle, then it is a parallelogram."

   a. Identify the hypothesis and the conclusion.

   b. Is the conditional statement true? Explain.

   c. Write the converse of the conditional statement. Is the converse true? Explain.

   d. Write the inverse of the conditional statement. Is the inverse true? Explain.

   e. Write the contrapositive of the conditional statement. Is the contrapositive true? Explain.

2. Consider the conditional statement "If a triangle is equilateral, then the triangle is equiangular."

   a. Identify the hypothesis and the conclusion.

   b. Is the conditional statement true? Explain.

   c. Write the converse of the conditional statement. Is the converse true? Explain.

   d. Write the inverse of the conditional statement. Is the inverse true? Explain.

   e. Write the contrapositive of the conditional statement. Is the contrapositive true? Explain.

Name _____ Date _____

3. Use an indirect two-column proof to show that the complements of congruent angles are congruent.

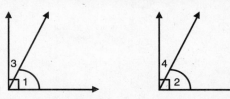

Given: $m\angle 1 = m\angle 2$, $m\angle 1 + m\angle 3 = 90°$, $m\angle 2 + m\angle 4 = 90°$

Prove: $m\angle 3 = m\angle 4$

4. Write an indirect paragraph proof to show that an isosceles triangle cannot have a base angle that is a right angle.

© Carnegie Learning

Name _____ Date _____

Three Angle Measure
Introduction to Trigonometry

1. Analyze triangle *ABC* and triangle *DEF*. Use ∠*A* and ∠*D* as the reference angles.

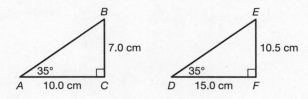

    a. Identify the leg opposite ∠*A*, the leg adjacent to ∠*A*, and the hypotenuse in △*ABC*.

    b. Calculate the length of the hypotenuse of triangle *ABC*. Round your answer to the nearest tenth.

    c. Calculate the ratios $\frac{\text{opposite}}{\text{hypotenuse}}$, $\frac{\text{adjacent}}{\text{hypotenuse}}$, and $\frac{\text{opposite}}{\text{adjacent}}$ for the reference angle in triangle *ABC*. Round your answers to the nearest thousandth if necessary.

9

d. Describe the relationship between $\triangle ABC$ and $\triangle DEF$. Explain your reasoning.

e. Calculate the length of the hypotenuse in $\triangle DEF$ without using the Pythagorean Theorem. Explain your reasoning.

f. Calculate the ratios $\dfrac{\text{opposite}}{\text{hypotenuse}}$, $\dfrac{\text{adjacent}}{\text{hypotenuse}}$, and $\dfrac{\text{opposite}}{\text{adjacent}}$ for the reference angle in $\triangle DEF$. Round your answers to the nearest thousandth if necessary.

g. Compare the values of the three ratios for $\triangle ABC$ and $\triangle DEF$. What do you observe? Why do you think this is true?

Name _____ Date _____

The Tangent Ratio
Tangent Ratio, Cotangent Ratio, and Inverse Tangent

Use the tangent ratio, the cotangent ratio, or the inverse tangent to solve for *x*. Round each answer to the nearest tenth.

1.

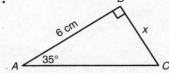

2.

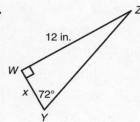

3.

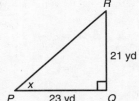

4.

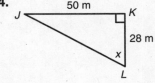

5. A roof truss is shown. Use the figure to complete parts (a) through (d).
Round each answer to the nearest hundredth.

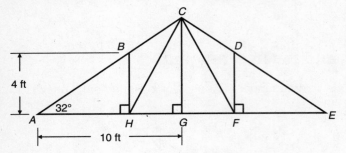

a. Determine the height *CG* of the roof truss.

b. Determine *AH*.

c. Determine the measure of angle *HCG*.

d. Determine the length *CH* of the support beam.

Name _____ Date _____

The Sine Ratio
Sine Ratio, Cosecant Ratio, and Inverse Sine

Use the sine ratio, the cosecant ratio, or the inverse sine to solve for x. Round each answer to the nearest tenth.

1.

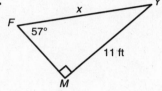

2.

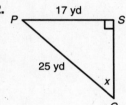

3.

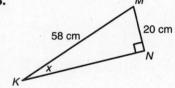

4.

5. A roof truss is shown in the following figure. Use the figure to complete parts (a) through (d). Round each answer to the nearest hundredth.

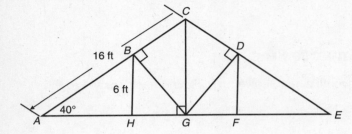

   a. Determine the height *CG* of the roof truss.

   b. Determine *AB*.

   c. Determine the measure of angle *BGC*.

   d. Determine the length *BG* of the support beam.

Name _____ Date _____

The Cosine Ratio
Cosine Ratio, Secant Ratio, and Inverse Cosine

Use the cosine ratio, the secant ratio, or the inverse cosine to solve for *x*. Round each answer to the nearest tenth.

1.

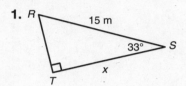

2.

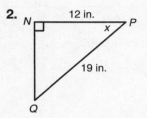

3.

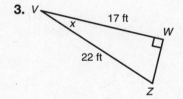

4.

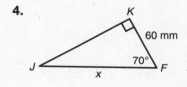

5. A bridge is shown in the following figure. Use the figure and the fact that △AGC is congruent to
△EGC to complete parts (a) through (e). Round each answer to the nearest tenth.

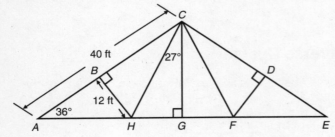

a. Determine the width *AE* of the bridge.

b. Determine the height *CG* of the bridge.

c. Determine *CH*.

Name _____ Date _____

    d. Determine the measure of ∠*BHC*.

    e. Does $\overline{CH}$ bisect ∠*ACG*? Explain your reasoning.

Name _____ Date _____

We Complement Each Other!
Complement Angle Relationships

1. An aircraft uses its radar to locate another aircraft that is 8000 feet away at a 12° angle of depression.

   a. Draw a figure to model this situation. Label the angle of depression and the hypotenuse. Label the side adjacent to the angle of depression as x and the side opposite the angle of depression as y.

   b. Calculate the vertical distance between the two aircraft. Round the distance to the nearest tenth.

   c. Calculate the horizontal distance between the two aircraft. Round the distance to the nearest tenth.

2. A pilot and co-pilot are performing a test run in a new airplane. The pilot is required to take off and fly in a straight path at an angle of elevation that is between 33 and 35 degrees until the plane reaches an altitude of 10,000 feet. When the plane reaches 10,000 feet, the co-pilot will take over.

a. Draw a figure to model this situation. Label the angle of elevation and the side opposite the angle of elevation. Label the side adjacent to the angle of elevation as x and the hypotenuse as y.

b. Determine the minimum and maximum horizontal distance between the point of take-off and the point at which the co-pilot takes over. Round each distance to the nearest tenth.

c. What is the minimum distance that the pilot flies the plane? What is the maximum distance that the pilot flies the plane? Round each distance to the nearest tenth.

Name _____ Date _____

Time to Derive!
Deriving the Triangle Area Formula, the Law of Sines, and the Law of Cosines

1. Emily and Joe are designing a fenced backyard play space for their children Max and Caroline. They start out by considering two designs for a triangular play space. They have made measurements in their yard and determined that either design would fit into the space that is available.

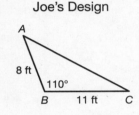

Emily's Design   Joe's Design

a. Explain how Emily and Joe can use trigonometry to calculate the area and perimeter of the possible play spaces.

b. Calculate the area of the play space for each design.

9

c. Calculate the perimeter of the play space for each design.

d. Which design do you think Emily and Joe should choose? Explain your reasoning.

2. Emily's brother-in-law Chris is an architect. She has asked him to design the placement of the playground equipment in her children's new play space. He sent her a diagram of the play space with the measurements shown.

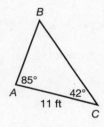

a. Explain how Emily can calculate the area and perimeter of the play space in Chris's design.

Name _____ Date _____

b. Calculate the area of the play space for Chris's design.

c. Calculate the perimeter of the play space for Chris's design.

Name _____ Date _____

Squares and Rectangles
Properties of Squares and Rectangles

1. In quadrilateral *VWXY*, segments *VX* and *WY* bisect each other, and are perpendicular and congruent. Is this enough information to conclude that quadrilateral *VWXY* is a square? Explain.

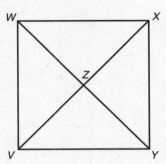

Quadrilateral *PQRS* is a rectangle with diagonals *PR* and *QS*.

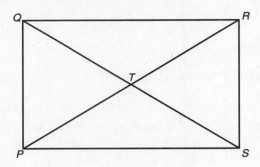

2. Name all parallel segments.

3. Name all congruent segments.

4. Name all right angles.

5. Name all congruent angles.

6. Name all congruent triangles.

Name _____ Date _____

Parallelograms and Rhombi
Properties of Parallelograms and Rhombi

Quadrilateral *PLGM* is a parallelogram.

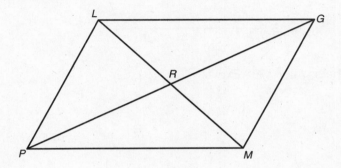

1. If $m\angle PLG = 124°$, what is $m\angle GMP$? Explain.

2. If $m\angle LPM = 56°$, what is $m\angle LGM$? Explain.

3. If the length of $\overline{LG}$ is 20 meters, what is *MP*? Explain.

4. If the length of $\overline{PR}$ is 12 inches, what is *GR*? Explain.

Quadrilateral *RHMB* is a rhombus.

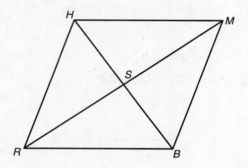

5. If *m∠HRB* = 70°, what is *m∠HMB*? Explain.

6. If *m∠RHB* = 55°, what is *m∠MHB*? Explain.

7. If the length of $\overline{RB}$ is 25 feet, what is *HR*? Explain.

8. If the length of $\overline{HS}$ is 18 centimeters, what is *SB*? Explain.

9. What is *m∠RSB*? Explain.

Name _____ Date _____

Kites and Trapezoids
Properties of Kites and Trapezoids

Quadrilateral *ABCD* is a kite.

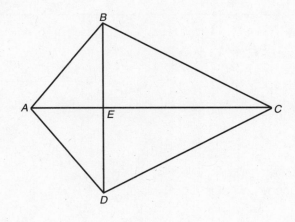

1. If *m∠ABC* = 95°, what is *m∠ADC*? Explain.

2. If *m∠BCE* = 34°, what is *m∠EBC*? Explain.

3. If the length of $\overline{AB}$ is 16 feet, what is *AD*? Explain.

4. If the length of $\overline{BD}$ is 25 feet, what is *ED*? Explain.

Quadrilateral *WXYZ* is an isosceles trapezoid.

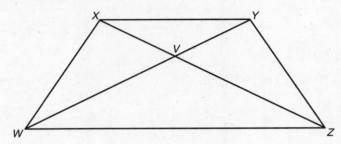

5. If *m∠XWZ* = 66°, what is *m∠YZW*? Explain.

6. If the length of $\overline{WY}$ is 10 inches, what is *ZX*? Explain.

7. If the length of $\overline{WX}$ is 7 inches, what is *ZY*? Explain.

Name _____ Date _____

Interior Angles of a Polygon
Sum of the Interior Angle Measures of a Polygon

Determine the measure of an interior angle of the given regular polygon.

1. regular nonagon

2. regular decagon

3. regular 15-gon

4. regular 47-gon

Determine the measure of the missing angle in each figure.

5.

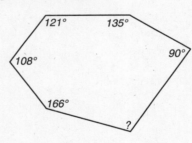

6.

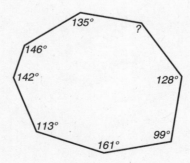

7. Use the figure to answer each question.

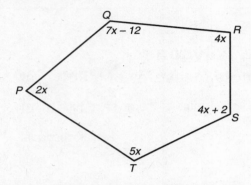

a. What is the sum of the measures of the interior angles of the polygon?

b. What is the value of *x*?

c. What is the measure of ∠*PTS*?

d. What is the measure of angle ∠*RQP*?

Name _____ Date _____

8. Suppose that the sum of the measures of the interior angles of a regular polygon is 157.5°. What type of polygon is it? Show your work and explain how you got your answer.

9. Suppose that the degree measure of each angle of a regular 12-gon can be represented by the expression $2x + 5$. Calculate the value of x.

Name _____ Date _____

Exterior and Interior Angle Measurement Interactions
Sum of the Exterior Angle Measures of a Polygon

Use the figure below to answer each question.

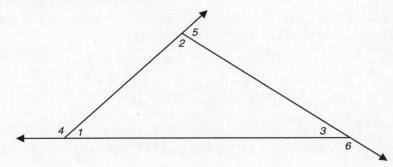

1. What is the sum of the measures of angles 1 and 4? Explain your reasoning.

2. What is the sum of the measures of angles 2 and 5? Explain your reasoning.

3. What is the sum of the measures of angles 3 and 6? Explain your reasoning.

4. What is the sum of the measures of angles 1, 2, 3, 4, 5, and 6? Explain your reasoning.

5. What is the sum of the measures of angles 1, 2, and 3? Explain your reasoning.

6. What is the difference of the sum of the measures of angles 1, 2, 3, 4, 5, and 6 and the sum of the measures of angles 1, 2, and 3? What does this demonstrate?

7. If a regular polygon has 30 sides, what is the measure of each exterior angle? Explain your reasoning.

8. The degree measure of each exterior angle of a regular octagon is represented by the expression $7x - 4$. Solve for x.

Name _____ Date _____

Quadrilateral Family
Categorizing Quadrilaterals Based on Their Properties

List all types of quadrilaterals with the given characteristics.

1. The quadrilateral has four right angles.

2. The quadrilateral has four congruent sides.

3. Exactly one pair of opposite sides of the quadrilateral is parallel.

4. Exactly two pairs of opposite sides of the quadrilateral are parallel.

5. Opposite angles of the quadrilateral are congruent.

6. Exactly two pairs of adjacent sides are congruent.

7. The sum of the measures of the interior angles of the quadrilateral is 360°.

8. The sum of the measures of the exterior angles of the quadrilateral is 360°.

9. The diagonals of the quadrilateral are congruent.

10. The diagonals of the quadrilateral do not bisect each other.

11. Quadrilateral *ABCD* has congruent diagonals that are perpendicular to each other. What type of quadrilateral is *ABCD*?

12. Quadrilateral *JKLM* has consecutive vertex angles that are supplementary but not congruent. If the diagonals bisect the vertex angles, what type of quadrilateral is *JKLM*?

Name _____ Date _____

Name That Quadrilateral!
Classifying Quadrilaterals on the Coordinate Plane

1. Analyze points *A*, *B*, and *C*. Locate point *D* so that the figure is an isosceles trapezoid.

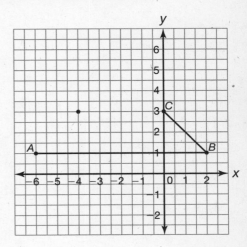

Classify the quadrilateral as a trapezoid, rectangle, rhombus, or square.

2. *A*(1, 3) *B*(5, 4) *C*(4, 0) *D*(0, −1)

3. *A*(0, −3) *B*(−4, 1) *C*(−6, −1) *D*(−2, −5)

Name _____ Date _____

Riding a Ferris Wheel
Introduction to Circles

Circle *C* is shown. Identify the indicated components of circle *C*.

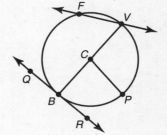

1. Name the chord(s).

2. Name the tangent(s).

3. Name the secant(s).

4. Name the central angle(s).

5. Name the inscribed angle(s).

6. Name the major arc(s).

7. Name the minor arc(s).

8. Name the semicircle(s).

Draw the indicated part using each given circle.

9. Draw chord *ST* using circle *C*.

10. Draw tangent *BC* using circle *S*, where *B* is the point of tangency.

11. Draw secant *LM* using circle *P*.

12. Draw central angle *XYZ* using circle *Y*.

13. Draw inscribed angle *JKL* using circle *D*.

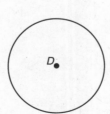

Name _____ Date _____

Take the Wheel
Central Angles, Inscribed Angles, and Intercepted Arcs

Use circle S to answer each question. Explain your reasoning.

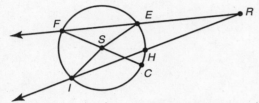

1. Suppose that $m\widehat{CE} = 59°$. What is $m\widehat{CFE}$?

2. Suppose that $m\angle CSI = 124°$. What is $m\widehat{FI}$?

3. Suppose that $m\widehat{CE} = 55°$. What is $m\angle EFC$?

4. Suppose that $m\angle FSI = 71°$. What is $m\widehat{IC}$?

5. In circle *E* shown, $m\angle ANG = 74°$.

    a. Determine $m\angle AEG$.

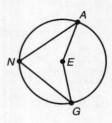

    b. Determine $m\widehat{ANG}$.

6. In circle *H* shown, $m\widehat{CA} = 105°$, $m\widehat{EA} = 47°$, and $m\widehat{ET} = 100°$.

    a. Determine $m\angle ETC$.

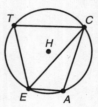

    b. Determine $m\angle TCE$.

    c. Determine $m\angle CAE$.

    d. Determine $m\angle TEA$.

Name _____ Date _____

Manhole Covers
Measuring Angles Inside and Outside of Circles

1. In circle *P* shown, $m\overset{\frown}{DE} = 75°$ and $m\overset{\frown}{NA} = 49°$. Determine $m\angle DTE$.

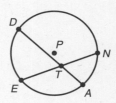

2. In circle *K* shown, $m\overset{\frown}{DN} = 144°$ and $m\angle NCA = 68°$. Determine $m\overset{\frown}{EA}$.

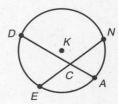

3. In circle *O* shown, m$\overset{\frown}{SN}$ = 55° and m$\overset{\frown}{HA}$ = 35°. Determine m∠*SCH*.

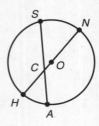

4. In circle *X* shown, m$\overset{\frown}{AS}$ = 11° and m$\overset{\frown}{MS}$ = 104°. Determine m∠*DCM*.

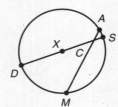

5. In circle *S* shown, m$\overset{\frown}{ER}$ = 38° and m$\overset{\frown}{OT}$ = 121°. Determine m∠*OUT*.

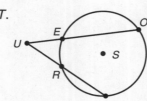

Name _____ Date _____

6. In circle *M* shown, $\overline{XE}$ is a diameter of the circle and $m\widehat{XT} = 132°$.
Draw a chord that connects points *X* and *T*. Then determine $m\angle XUT$.

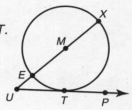

7. In circle *G* shown, $OH = ES$, $m\widehat{OH} = 41°$, and
$m\widehat{HE} = 171°$. Determine $m\angle EUH$.

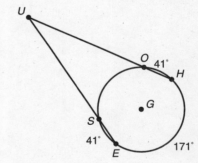

© Carnegie Learning

8. In circle *B* shown, $m\widehat{HE} = 99°$.

   a. Determine $m\angle HUE$.

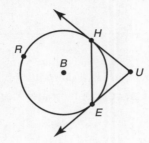

   b. Determine $m\angle BHU$.

9. In circle *T* shown, $m\angle RCE = 57°$ and $m\widehat{RE} = 141°$.
Determine $m\widehat{BL}$.

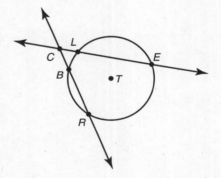

Name _____ Date _____

Color Theory
Chords

1. Use circle *T* to complete parts (a) through (g).

a. Draw an inscribed right angle in circle *T*. Label each point where the angle intersects the circle. What is the name of the right angle?

b. Draw the chord determined by the inscribed right angle. What is the name of the chord?

c. What else do you know about the chord determined by an inscribed right angle?

d. Draw a second inscribed right angle in circle *T*. Label each point where the angle intersects the circle. What is the name of the second right angle?

e. Draw the chord determined by the second inscribed right angle. What is the name of the chord?

f. What else do you know about the chord determined by the second inscribed right angle?

g. Describe the relationship between the arcs that correspond to the chords you named in parts (b) and (e). Explain your reasoning.

h. Do you think every inscribed right angle will determine the longest chord of the circle, which is the diameter of the circle? Explain your reasoning.

2. The figure shows a section of a circle. Draw two chords and construct their perpendicular bisectors to locate the center of the circle. Explain your work.

3. In circle *G* shown below, *MG* = 1.84 centimeters, *GL* = 1.98 centimeters, *m∠GLH* = 90°, and *m∠GMK* = 90°. Determine which chord is longer, *IH* or *JK*. Explain your reasoning.

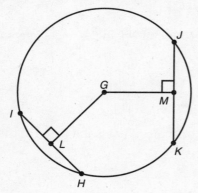

Name _____ Date _____

Solar Eclipses
Tangents and Secants

1. Use circle *O* to complete parts (a) through (h).

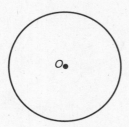

a. Draw a tangent to circle *O*. Label the point of tangency as point *A*.

b. Label another point on the tangent you drew in part (a) as point *B*.

c. Draw a second tangent line to circle *O* that passes through point *B*. Label this second point of tangency as point *C*.

d. Draw the radii $\overline{OA}$ and $\overline{OC}$.

e. What is $m\angle OAB$? Explain your reasoning.

f. What is $m\angle OCB$? Explain your reasoning.

11

   g. Use a protractor to determine the measure of ∠AOC.

   h. What is m∠ABC? Explain your reasoning.

2. In the figure shown, rays *LJ* and *LH* are tangent to circle *K*, and the measure of angle *LJH* is 71°. What is the measure of angle *JLH*? Explain your reasoning.

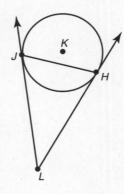

3. In the figure shown, *WV* = 36 inches, point *X* is a midpoint of segment *WV*, and *YV* = 40 inches. What is *YZ*? Explain your reasoning.

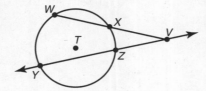

Name _____ Date _____

4. In the figure shown, line *FG* is tangent to circle *Q*, *BC* = 10 feet, and
   CG = 4 feet. What is *FG*? Explain your reasoning.

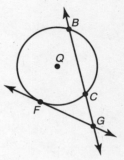

11

Name _____ Date _____

Replacement for a Carpenter's Square
Inscribed and Circumscribed Triangles and Quadrilaterals

1. In the figure shown, △ABC is inscribed in circle D and m∠A = 55°. What is m∠C? Explain your reasoning.

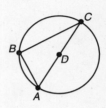

2. In the figure shown, △XYZ is inscribed in circle W and XY = YZ. What is m∠X? Explain your reasoning.

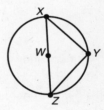

3. In the figure shown, △RST is inscribed in circle Q, RS = 18 centimeters, and ST = 24 centimeters. What is RT? Explain your reasoning.

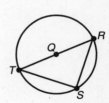

4. In the figure shown, quadrilateral *FGHJ* is inscribed in circle *K*, $m\angle F = 112°$, and $m\angle G = 87°$. What are $m\angle H$ and $m\angle J$? Explain your reasoning.

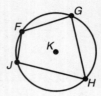

5. In the figure shown, quadrilateral *LMNP* is inscribed in circle *R*, $m\angle P = 57°$, and $m\angle L = m\angle N$. What are $m\angle M$, $m\angle L$, and $m\angle N$? Explain your reasoning.

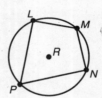

12

Name _____ Date _____

Gears
Arc Length

1. In circle *A* shown describe the difference between the measure of minor arc *BC* and the length of minor arc *BC*.

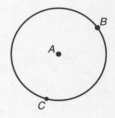

2. In circle *E* shown, the radius of the circle is 16 centimeters and m∠*JSB* is 40°. Determine the length of $\widehat{JB}$.

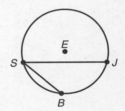

3. In circle *I* shown, the radius is 6 millimeters and $m\overset{\frown}{HC}$ is 80°.

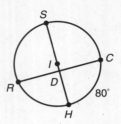

   a. Determine the length of $\overset{\frown}{SC}$ in millimeters.

   b. Determine the measure of $\overset{\frown}{SC}$ in radians.

4. In circle *H* shown, the length of $\overset{\frown}{SJ}$ is 24π centimeters and $m\angle JOS$ is 80°. Determine the length of a diameter of circle *H*.

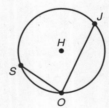

Name _____ Date _____

Playing Darts
Sectors and Segments of a Circle

In circle C shown, △ABC is an equilateral triangle and AC = 10 inches.

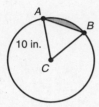

1. Calculate the area of sector *ACB*. Express your answer in terms of π and as a decimal rounded to the nearest hundredth.

2. The height of △*ABC* is approximately 8.66 inches. Calculate the area of △*ABC*.

3. Calculate the area of segment *AB* of circle *C*. Express your answer in terms of π and as a decimal rounded to the nearest hundredth.

In circle *A*, the radius is 18 centimeters and △*ABC* is an equilateral triangle.

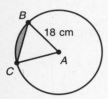

4. Calculate the area of sector *CAB*. Express your answer in terms of π and as a decimal rounded to the nearest hundredth.

5. Calculate the area of segment *BC*. Express your answer in terms of π and as a decimal rounded to the nearest hundredth.

12

Name _____ Date _____

In circle *S*, the radius is 22 feet and *m∠RST* = 90°.

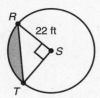

6. Calculate the area of sector *RST*. Express your answer in terms of π and as a decimal rounded to the nearest hundredth.

7. Calculate the area of segment *RT*. Express your answer in terms of π and as a decimal rounded to the nearest hundredth.

12

Name _____ Date _____

Circle K. Excellent!
Circle Problems

1. Deborah would like to put edging along the circular edge of her flower garden. The following is a diagram of her flower garden. How much edging will she need if she just puts it along the circular part? Show all of your work and use 3.14 for π. Round your answer to the nearest hundredth if necessary.

2. Jonathan has a circular pool in his backyard with an 18-foot diameter. He would like to pave a 6-foot-wide circle around his pool. How much paved area will Jonathan have around his pool? Show all of your work and use 3.14 for π.

12

3. A company has a circular card table with a 4-foot diameter. They want to remove a portion to provide a place for the dealer to stand. See the following diagram. How much surface area of the table will be left for those who are sitting at the table? Show all your work and use 3.14 for π. Round your answer to the nearest hundredth if necessary.

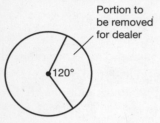

Portion to
be removed
for dealer

120°

4. Geneva has a circular table with a 6-foot diameter that she would like to put in her new kitchen. In order for it to fit up against the wall, she must cut off the portion of the table that is shaded in the following diagram. The measure of the central angle is 100°. How much surface area will she lose when she removes this part of the table? Show all your work and use 3.14 for π.

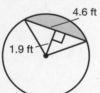

4.6 ft

1.9 ft

Name _____ Date _____

The Coordinate Plane
Circles and Polygons on the Coordinate Plane

1. In circle C, chords $\overline{AB}$ and $\overline{DE}$ intersect at point F. Use the given information to algebraically show that if two chords intersect, then the product of the lengths of the segments of one chord is equal to the product of the lengths of the segments of the other chord.

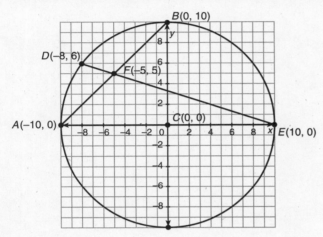

2. Quadrilateral *WXYZ* is a kite. Draw the quadrilateral formed by connecting the midpoints of the sides of the kite and label this quadrilateral *ABCD*. Then classify quadrilateral *ABCD*. Show all your work.

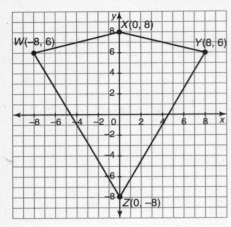

13

Name _____ Date _____

3. Triangle *JKL* is inscribed in circle *D*.

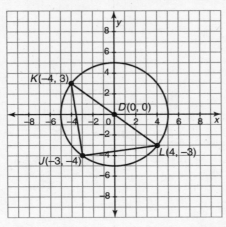

a. Show that △*JKL* is an isosceles right triangle.

b. Is a triangle inscribed in a circle always an isosceles right triangle or only under certain conditions? Explain how you know.

Name _____ Date _____

Bring On the Algebra
Deriving the Equation for a Circle

1. Write an equation in standard form for:

    a. a circle with a center at M $(-4, 2)$ and a radius of 3.

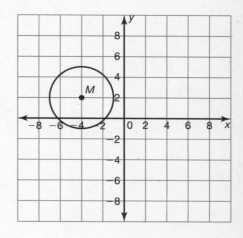

    b. a circle with the same center as the circle M, but whose circumference is 20 times that of circle M.

    c. a circle with a center at L $(3, 3)$ and a radius of 5.

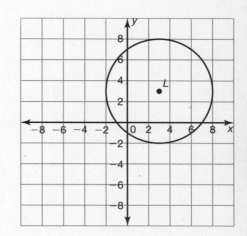

    d. a circle with the same center as the circle L, but whose area is 20 times that of circle L.

13

2. Determine if each equation represents a circle. If so, describe the location of the center and radius.

 a. $x^2 + y^2 - 4x + 6y + 9 = 0$

 b. $4x^2 + 4y^2 - 8x - 20y - 30 = 0$

 c. $3x^2 + y^2 + 3x + 9y + 15 = 0$

Name _____ Date _____

Is That Point on the Circle?
Determining Points on a Circle

1. Consider circle *P* centered at the origin with a radius of 4 units as shown.

   a. Verify that point *K* (1, $\sqrt{15}$) lies on circle *P*.

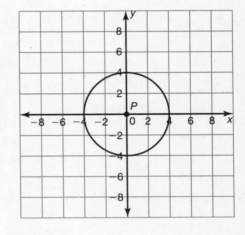

   b. Use symmetry to determine three more points on circle *P*.

2. Consider circle *T* with its center point located at (2, 3) with a radius of $3\sqrt{2}$ units as shown.

   a. Verify that point *R* (5, 0) lies on circle *T*.

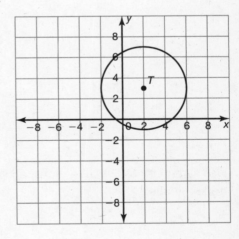

   b. Use symmetry to determine three more points on circle *P*.

13

3. Maddie brought home a new puppy, Ralph, which she needs to introduce to her current dog, Ellie. She ties Ellie in the middle of her backyard. She ties a shorter rope, exactly 4 feet to the east and 4 feet north of Ellie's rope, for her new puppy, Ralph. Based upon the graph, the dogs can meet at the point (3, 4).

   a. Graph the range each dog will be able to travel on their rope. Use the origin as the place where Ellie is tied down. Show your work.

   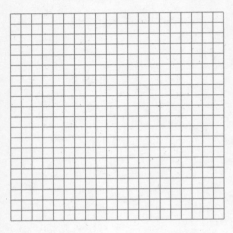

   b. Use symmetry to describe the location of the other point that is on the very edge of both of the dogs' ranges.

Name _____ Date _____

The Parabola
Equation of a Parabola

1. Determine the vertex, axis of symmetry, the value of p, the directrix, the focus, and the concavity for each parabola. Then graph the parabola.

a. $x^2 = 3y$

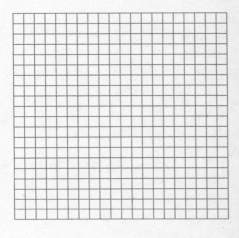

b. $2y^2 = x$

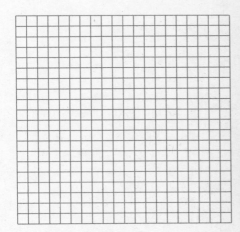

2. Determine the equation of each parabola with the given focus and directrix. Let (x, y) represent a point on the parabola.

   a. focus: $(0, 3)$; directrix: $y = -3$

   b. focus: $(-4, 0)$; directrix: $x = 4$

   c. focus: $(7, 0)$; directrix: $x = -7$

Name _____ Date _____

Simply Parabolic
More with Parabolas

1. Use the distance formula to determine an equation for all the points equidistant from the given point and line.

    a. $(-3, 4.5)$ and $y = 3.5$

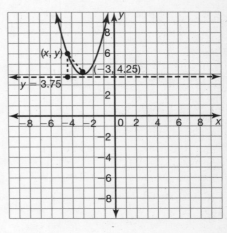

    b. $(3, -1)$ and $x = 7$

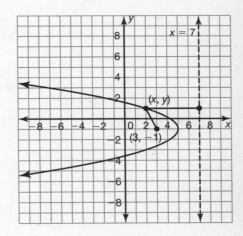

2. Determine the vertex, axis of symmetry, the value of p, the directrix, the focus, and the concavity for each parabola. Then graph the parabola.

   a. $x = -(y - 2)^2 + 3$

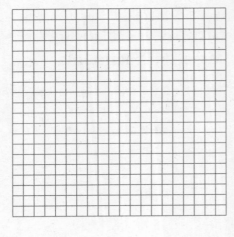

   b. $x^2 - 8x - 4y - 4 = 0$

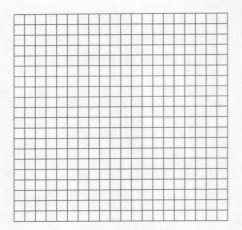

Name _____ Date _____

3. Write an equation in standard form for each parabola. Then graph and label the parabola.

   a. A parabola with a vertex of (8, 6) and a focus of (6, 6).

   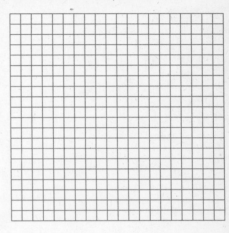

   b. A parabola with a vertex of (1, 0) and a directrix of $y = -3$.

   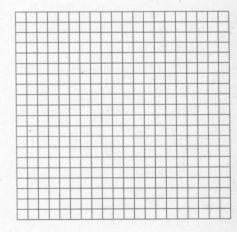

13

Name _____ Date _____

These Are a Few of My Favorite Things
Modeling Probability

1. A board game includes the spinner shown in the figure that players must use to advance a game piece around the board.

a. What is the sample space if a player spins the spinner shown one time?

b. What is the probability of spinning the number 3, $P(3)$?

c. What is the probability of spinning a number greater than 1?

d. Construct the probability model for spinning the spinner.

e. Is this a uniform probability model or a non-uniform probability model? Explain how you know.

f. What is the probability of a spin not resulting in a 4?

14

2. In this game, players can earn different types of tokens as they move around the board. If a player lands on certain spaces, the player can randomly choose a token from a box. The token is then replaced before the next player's turn.

6 tokens   4 tokens   2 tokens

   a. What is the sample space if a player randomly chooses one of the tokens?

   b. What is the probability of choosing a pyramid, *P*(pyramid)?

   c. What is the probability of choosing a cube?

   d. Construct the probability model for choosing one of the tokens.

   e. Is this a uniform probability model or a non-uniform probability model? Explain how you know.

   f. What is the probability of choosing a token that is not a cylinder?

14

Name _____ Date _____

It's in the Cards
Compound Sample Spaces

1. While playing a board game, a player randomly chooses one card from each of the two decks, and then replaces the cards in the decks.

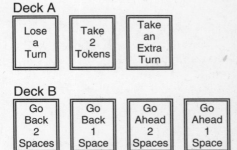

Deck A

| Lose a Turn | Take 2 Tokens | Take an Extra Turn |

Deck B

| Go Back 2 Spaces | Go Back 1 Space | Go Ahead 2 Spaces | Go Ahead 1 Space |

a. What are the actions?

b. What are the outcomes of each action?

c. Do the outcomes of each action belong to disjoint sets or intersecting sets? Explain.

d. Write an organized list that represents the sample space.

14

    e. Are the events in each outcome of the sample space independent or dependent?

    f. Determine the size of the sample space using the Counting Principle. Show your calculation.

2. Amanda randomly chooses a card from a deck of six cards, without replacing it, then chooses another card. The cards are numbered 1 through 6.

    a. What are the actions?

    b. What are the outcomes of each action?

    c. Do the outcomes of each action belong to disjoint sets or intersecting sets? Explain.

    d. Sketch a tree diagram that represents the sample space.

    e. Are the events in each outcome of the sample space independent or dependent?

    f. Determine the size of the sample space using the Counting Principle. Show your calculation.

© Carnegie Learning

14

Name _____ Date _____

And?
Compound Probability with "And"

1. Suppose a player chooses cards from the two decks shown. The subsets of cards are labeled C1 to C7 (see figure).

   a. A player chooses one card from Deck A and one card from Deck B. What is the probability that the player will choose cards C1 and C4?

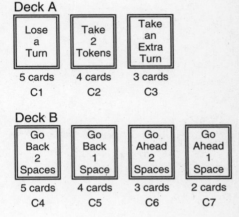

Deck A

Lose a Turn	Take 2 Tokens	Take an Extra Turn
5 cards	4 cards	3 cards
C1	C2	C3

Deck B

Go Back 2 Spaces	Go Back 1 Space	Go Ahead 2 Spaces	Go Ahead 1 Space
5 cards	4 cards	3 cards	2 cards
C4	C5	C6	C7

   b. A player chooses one card from Deck A and replaces it. Then the next player chooses one card from Deck A. What is the probability that both players will choose a C2 card?

14

c. A player chooses two cards at the same time from Deck B. What is the probability that the player will choose two C5 cards?

d. A player chooses one card from Deck A and one card from Deck B. What is the probability of not choosing a C1 card from Deck A and the probability of not choosing a C7 card from Deck B?

e. A player chooses one card from Deck A and then, without replacing it, chooses another card from Deck A. What is the probability that the first card will be a C2 and the second card will not be a C2?

Name _____ Date _____

2. The board game includes both the spinner and the set of tokens shown in the figure.

a. A player spins the spinner once and then randomly chooses a token. What is the probability that the spinner will land on a 4 and the player will choose a cube token?

6 tokens   4 tokens   2 tokens

b. A player spins the spinner twice. What is the probability that the second spin will land on a 3?

c. A player chooses a token from the set, replaces it, and then chooses another token from the set. What is the probability that the first token chosen will be a cube and the second will be a disk?

d. A player chooses two tokens from the set at the same time. What is the probability that both will be pyramids?

e. A player spins the spinner once and then randomly chooses a token. What is the probability that the spinner will not land on a 3 and the player will choose a disk token?

14

Name _____ Date _____

    f. A player randomly chooses three tokens at once from the set. What is the probability that the first two tokens are cubes?

Name _____ Date _____

Or?
Compound Probability with "Or"

1. Two decks of cards are used for a game.

   a. A player chooses one card from Deck A and one card from Deck B. What is the probability that the player will choose a C2 card from the first deck and a C6 card from the second deck?

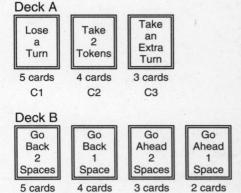

Deck A

Lose a Turn	Take 2 Tokens	Take an Extra Turn
5 cards C1	4 cards C2	3 cards C3

Deck B

Go Back 2 Spaces	Go Back 1 Space	Go Ahead 2 Spaces	Go Ahead 1 Space
5 cards C4	4 cards C5	3 cards C6	2 cards C7

b. A player chooses one card from Deck A and one card from Deck B. What is the probability that the player will choose a C3 card from the first deck or a C5 card from the second deck?

c. A player chooses two cards from Deck A. What is the probability that the player will choose a C1 card first or a C2 card second?

Name _____ Date _____

   d. A player chooses two cards from Deck B. What is the probability that the player will choose a C5 card first or a C4 card second?

2. Consider the spinner and the set of tokens shown in the figure.

   a. A player spins the spinner one time and then randomly chooses a token. What is the probability that the spinner will land on a 2 or the player will choose a pyramid?

6 tokens   4 tokens   2 tokens

b. A player spins the spinner two times. What is the probability that the spinner will land on a number greater than 1 the first time or on a number greater than 2 the second time?

c. A player spins the spinner one time and then randomly chooses a token. What is the probability that the spinner will not land on a 2 or the player will not choose a disk?

Name _____ Date _____

   d. A player spins the spinner two times. What is the probability that the spinner will land on a 1 the first time or on a 4 the second time?

   e. A player spins the spinner one time and then randomly chooses a token. What is the probability that the spinner will land on a 2 or the player will choose a cube?

14

Name _____ Date _____

And, Or, and More!
Calculating Compound Probability

1. A game includes a deck of cards with an animal picture on each card. The table shows the numbers of each type of card. Suppose each time a card is chosen, the card is replaced before another card is chosen.

Number of Cards	Animal on Card
8	lion
6	giraffe
10	monkey
12	elephant
4	panda bear

a. A child draws out two cards. What is the probability that the first card will have a monkey on it and the second card will have an elephant on it?

b. A child draws out two cards. What is the probability that the first card will have a lion on it or the second card will have a giraffe on it?

14

c. A child draws out two cards. What is the probability that the second card will have a panda bear on it?

d. A child draws out three cards. What is the probability that the first card will have a lion on it, and the third will have a monkey on it?

e. A child draws out five cards. What is the probability that they will all have a different animal on them?

Name _____ Date _____

2. A game includes a deck of cards with an animal picture on each card. The table shows the numbers of each type of card. When a card is chosen, it is not replaced in the deck.

Number	Animal on Card
8	lion
6	giraffe
10	monkey
12	elephant
4	panda bear

   a. A child draws out two cards. What is the probability that the first card will have an elephant on it and the second card will have a lion on it?

   b. A child draws out two cards. What is the probability that the first card will have a monkey on it or the second card will have a panda bear on it?

c. A child draws out three cards. What is the probability that the second card will have a lion on it?

d. A child draws out two cards. What is the probability that the first card will have a panda bear on it or the second card will have a giraffe on it?

e. A child draws out three cards. What is the probability that the second and third cards will display elephants?

Name _____ Date _____

    f. A child draws out two cards. What is the probability that the first card will have a lion on it or the second card will have a monkey on it?

14

Name _____ Date _____

Do You Have a Better Chance of Winning the Lottery or Getting Struck By Lightning?
Investigate Magnitude through Theoretical Probability and Experimental Probability

1. A spinner with 8 equal parts, labeled 1 to 8, is used in a board game. You spin the spinner one time.

   a. What is the theoretical probability of the spinner landing on a 2?

   b. You spin the spinner 20 times, and 5 times is lands on a 2. What is the experimental probability of the spinner landing on a 2?

   c. Compare the theoretical probability and the experimental probability. Which is greater?

2. A spinner with 16 equal parts, labeled 1 to 16, is used in a board game. You spin the spinner one time. Another spinner has 6 equal parts, labeled 1 to 6. You spinner the spinner one time also.

   a. What is the theoretical probability of both spinners landing on a 4?

   b. You spin the first spinner 25 times, and 10 times is lands on a 4. You spin the second spinner 25 times, and 5 times is lands on a 4. What is the experimental probability of the both spinners landing on a 4?

   c. Compare the theoretical probability and the experimental probability. Which is greater?

3. Each number from 0 to 99 is written on a separate card. The cards are placed in a box, and you randomly draw out one card.

   a. What is the theoretical probability of drawing out a number less than 25? (Hint: Because 0 is included, there are 25 numbers less than 25.)

   b. Using the random number generator on a calculator, press **ENTER** 5 times to simulate 100 trials. How many times did a number 25 appear? What is the experimental probability of randomly obtaining a number less than 25?

   c. Compare the theoretical probability and the experimental probability. Which is greater?

   d. What is the theoretical probability of drawing out a number greater than 21 but less than 28?

   e. Use the random number generator again to simulate 100 trials. How many times did a number greater than 21 but less than 28 appear? What is the experimental probability of randomly obtaining a number in this range?

   f. Compare the theoretical probability and the experimental probability. Which is greater?

   g. Run another random number experiment, but this time use 200 trials. Describe your results for obtaining a number greater than 21 but less than 28. Are the results the same?

4. Describe the relationship between experimental probability and theoretical probability as the number of trials of an experiment increases.

Name _____ Date _____

Left, Left, Left, Right, Left
Compound Probability for Data Displayed in Two-Way Tables

1. Jermaine rolls two number cubes.

   a. Complete the two way table to represent all the possible products of the numbers rolled on two number cubes.

	1	2	3	4	5	6
1						
2						
3						
4						
5						
6						

   b. Create a frequency table with the product of the numbers rolled on the two number cubes and their frequency.

c. Use your two-way table and frequency table to answer each question.

   i. What is the probability of rolling an odd product?

   ii. What is the probability of rolling a product less than 10?

d. Use the converse of the multiplication rule to determine whether the events are independent.
   Explain your reasoning.

   i. rolling a 2 on the first number cube and rolling a 6 on the second number cube

Name _____ Date _____

    ii. rolling a 3 on the first number cube and a product equal to 20

2. A survey was taken of 24 households on Oak Street to compare the number of cars registered to the household and the number of people who live in the house. The responses are shown in the table.

   a. Complete the table. Write each result as a fraction and a percent rounded to the tenths place.

		Number of People in Household								Total	Rel. Freq.
		2		3		4		5			
		Freq.	Rel. Freq.	Freq.	Rel. Freq.	Freq.	Rel. Freq.	Freq.	Rel. Freq.		
Number of Cars	1	2		1		1		0			
	2	4		3		5		3			
	3	0		1		3		1			
Total											

   b. What is the probability that a randomly chosen house on Oak Street:

   i. has 2 cars?

   ii. has 3 people in the household?

   iii. has 4 people in the household and 3 cars?

   iv. has 5 people in the household and 2 cars?

Name _____ Date _____

It All Depends
Conditional Probability

1. Suppose you have 3 nickels, 1 quarter, and 1 penny in your pocket. You choose a coin, do not replace it, and then choose a second coin.

   a. Write an organized list to represent all of the possible outcomes.

   b. What is the probability of randomly picking a penny first, P(penny 1st)?

   c. What is the probability of picking a quarter first and a nickel second?

   d. What is the probability of picking a nickel second, given that a quarter is picked first?

2. Walt is selling candy outside the supermarket to raise money for new uniforms for the gymnastics team. The probability of a customer stopping to talk to Walt and buying some candy is $\frac{2}{9}$. The probability of a customer just stopping to talk to Walt is $\frac{5}{12}$. Fifty out of the 120 customers at the supermarket bought candy from Walt.

a. What is the probability of a customer buying candy from Walt given that they stopped to talk to him?

b. Are a customer talking to Walt and a customer buying candy from Walt independent or dependent events? Explain your reasoning.

Name _____ Date _____

3. A survey was taken to determine the number of students that own a dog and a cat as a pet. When a student from the survey is chosen at random, the probability that the student owns both a dog and a cat is $\frac{1}{12}$. When a student is chosen at random, the probability that the student owns a dog is $\frac{1}{4}$ and the probability the student owns a cat is $\frac{1}{3}$.

a. What is the probability that a student chosen at random who owns a dog also owns a cat?

b. Are "owning a dog" and "owning a cat" independent or dependent events? Explain your reasoning.

15

Name _____ Date _____

Counting
Permutations and Combinations

1. State whether each question uses permutations or combinations. Then calculate the answer.

   a. The Debate Club contains 13 members. They need to elect 3 members to the executive board: a president, vice president, and secretary. How many different executive boards are possible?

   b. Quentin used 7 websites during research for a report. How many different ways can he list the websites in his bibliography?

   c. Tyler has 28 songs on his computer. He is transferring 8 songs to his MP3 player. How many different ways can the songs be chosen?

   d. Josy is making a pattern with 2 squares, one triangle, and one circle. How many different patterns can Josy make?

   e. Sydney works at a kennel. She takes the 8 dogs at the kennel out for a walk in groups of 2. How many different groups of dogs can Sydney take?

2. Calculate the following probabilities.

    a. A field hockey team has 10 members and the coach randomly selects 2 players as captains for each game. What is the probability that coach chooses you and your best friend and captains?

    b. Germaine has 2 quarters, a nickel, and a penny that he is randomly placing on the table in a line. What is the probability that the order of the coins will be quarter, nickel, penny, quarter?

3. Calculate the number of arrangements.

    a. How many different 7-digit numbers can be written using the digits 1, 1, 2, 7, 7, 7, 8, and 9?

    b. How many different ways can the letters in the word GEOMETRY be arranged?

Name _____ Date _____

4. Mrs. Rynearson is a Kindergarten teacher. She asks her students to sit in a circle. Calculate the number of arrangements for each number of students.

   a. four students

   b. six students

Name _____ Date _____

Trials
Independent Trials

1. Bus drivers for the Townsende School District are hired from either in district or outside of the district. When Mr. Fine calls the transportation director, he is told that his sons have a $\frac{7}{10}$ change of having a bus driver that was hired from in district (*I*) and a $\frac{3}{10}$ chance of having a bus driver that was hired from outside the district (*O*). His two sons each ride a different bus to school, since one is at the elementary school and the other is at the middle school.

   a. What is the probability that the bus driver for both sons will be hired from inside of the district?

   b. What is the probability that the bus driver for both sons will be hired from outside of the district?

   c. What is the probability that one son will have a bus driver hired from inside of the district and the other will have a bus driver hired from outside of the district?

   d. Suppose Mr. Fine's daughter, who attends the high school, is also going to take a bus to school. What is the probability that Mr. Fine's sons will have a bus driver hired from inside of the district, but his daughter will have a bus driver hired from outside of the district?

2. A number cube has 5 green sides and 1 orange side.

   a. What is the probability of 4 green outcomes and 1 orange outcome when the number cube is rolled 5 times?

   b. What is the probability of 2 green outcomes and 2 orange outcomes when the number cube is rolled 4 times?

   c. What is the probability of 3 green outcomes and 4 orange outcomes when the number cube is rolled 7 times?

3. A bag contains 3 nickels and 1 penny. Coins are replaced in the bag after every choice.

   a. What is the probability of randomly choosing 4 nickels and one penny in 5 trials?

   b. What is the probability of randomly choosing 2 nickels and 3 pennies in 5 trials?

   c. What is the probability of randomly choosing 1 nickel and 5 pennies in 6 trials?

   d. What is the probability of randomly choosing 4 nickels and 3 pennies in 7 trials?

Name _____ Date _____

To Spin or Not to Spin
Expected Value

1. A dart is thrown and lands on random spot on each target. Determine the probability of hitting the shaded region. Write your answers as a percent rounded to the nearest tenth.

   a. The board shown is two circles inscribed inside a rectangle.

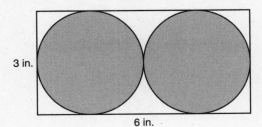

b. The board shown is a triangle and a trapezoid inside of a rectangle.

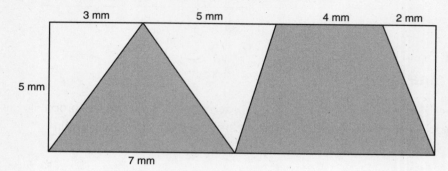

Name _____ Date _____

c. In the figure below, points *E*, *F*, *G* and *H* are midpoints. Both figures are squares. Let *x* represent the length of one side of the board.

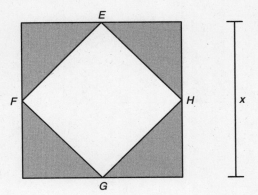

d. In the figure below, an octagon is inside of a square. The vertices of the octagon trisect the sides of the square. Let *x* represent the length of one side of the board.

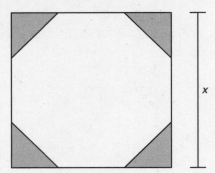

Name _____ Date _____

2. At a carnival, Jasmine is playing a game with the dartboard below. The dartboard has a rectangular
shaped top and a semicircle along the bottom. She throws a dart that lands randomly on the
dartboard, and wins the number of tickets shown in each region.

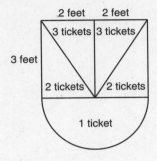

2 feet   2 feet

3 tickets 3 tickets

3 feet

2 tickets   2 tickets

1 ticket

a. Determine the areas you will need to know to calculate the expected value for the number of
tickets Jasmine will win.

b. Determine the probabilities you will need to know to calculate the expected value for the number of tickets Jasmine will win.

c. What is the expected value for the number of tickets Jasmine will win?